Diffraction of X-rays by Proteins, Nucleic Acids and Viruses

Herbert R. WILSON Ph.D.

Carnegie Laboratory of Physics
University of St. Andrews
Queen's College, Dundee

New York

St Martin's Press

1966

Library of Congress Catalog Card Number: 66–18554

Printed in Northern Ireland at The Universities Press, Belfast

Preface

One branch of Biology has always been concerned with the structure of living matter. In this field of study, the development of physical techniques has played an important part in extending the studies to increasingly finer levels of detail, which, during the last three decades, have reached the molecular level. One of the most fruitful physical techniques during this latter period has been that of x-ray diffraction, a method whereby the three-dimensional structure of biological molecules can be determined. Molecular structure determination forms an essential part of Molecular Biology, which is concerned with explaining how biological processes function at a molecular level. This term, Molecular Biology, was proposed by W. T. Astbury, who was one of the pioneers in applying x-ray diffraction methods to investigate biological structures.

The object of this monograph is to outline the principles of x-ray diffraction methods and to discuss the results of their application in the study of proteins, nucleic acids, nucleoproteins and viruses. It should be of primary interest to students taking courses in biophysics, molecular biology, biology and biochemistry. It should also be of interest to some students of medicine, chemistry and physics. While the level is most suitable for second and third year undergraduates and postgraduate students, some of the material should not be too advanced for interested first year students.

The first chapter introduces, at a very elementary level, some of the basic concepts that are relevant to the consideration of molecular structures. Chapter 2 is concerned with the theory of x-ray diffraction, and, as such, is more specialized than the other chapters. Chapters 3, 4 and 5 respectively, describe the results of x-ray diffraction studies of proteins, nucleic acids, and nucleoproteins and viruses.

I should like to express my thanks to the many friends and colleagues who supplied prints for illustrations and gave permission to reproduce from their original papers; to Professor G. D. Preston, Dr. J. Iball and Dr. Stewart McGavin for valuable comments on the manuscript, and to Miss Pearl M. Mitchell for typing it.

I should also like to take this opportunity of expressing my gratitude to Professor E. A. Owen, Professor G. D. Preston, Professor Sir John Randall and Professor Maurice Wilkins, who, at various times, have guided and encouraged me in my work.

Dundee   H. R. W.
1965

Acknowledgements

It is a pleasure to thank the following bodies for permission to reproduce published illustrations; The Royal Society for Fig. 2.20; Istituto Lombardo for Figs. 3.2 and 3.3; Proceedings of the National Academy of Science, U.S.A., for Figs. 3.6 and 3.7; Biochimica et Biophysica Acta for Figs. 3.8, 3.9 and Plate 2(c); Acta Crystallographica for Figs. 3.10 and 5.3; Nature for Figs. 3.12, 3.13, 3.15, 3.16, 3.17, 3.18,3.19, 5.1 (a) and Plates 1(a), 1(c), 1(d), 6(a), 6(b) and 7(a); Journal of Molecular Biology for Figs. 3.14, 4.11 and Plates 2(a), 3(b), 4(b) and 8(c); J. and A. Churchill Ltd. for Fig. 5.4; Cold Spring Harbor Symposium on Quantitative Biology for Fig. 5.1(b) and Plates 5(d) and 7(b); Academic Press for Fig. 5.5; Biophysical Journal for Fig. 5.6; The Faraday Society for Plate 1(b); Pergamon Press for Plate 3(c); the American Association for the Advancement of Science for Plate 5(b).

Contents

Introduction

X-rays were discovered by Röntgen in 1895, and this was followed by a period of intensive investigation of their properties. In 1912, von Laue suggested that if crystals were built up of a regular arrangement of atoms, then x-rays should be diffracted by a crystal in a similar way to the diffraction of light by a diffraction grating. Von Laue's suggestion was verified experimentally by Friedrich and Knipping.

The discovery of x-ray diffraction was soon followed by the investigations of W. H. and W. L. Bragg, and the interpretation of the diffraction process was greatly simplified by W. L. Bragg's concept of the reflection of x-rays from crystal planes.

The discovery of x-ray diffraction also marked the birth of x-ray crystallography, whereby it is possible to use the diffraction patterns to reveal the atomic positions in a crystal. Starting with a study of inorganic crystals, the method was soon extended to the study of minerals and relatively simple organic molecules, and later to complex organic and biological molecules.

The success of x-ray diffraction studies of biological molecules since the early 1950's has played an important part in the spectacular advances that have taken place in the field of molecular biology. It is with these studies that we shall be mainly concerned.

Partly from the results of single crystal x-ray analysis of amino acids and dipeptides, Pauling and Corey, in 1951, proposed the α-helix as the basic structure of a group of fibrous proteins which occur in hair, muscle, skin and blood. The similarity in the structure of the members of this group had been indicated earlier by Astbury. In 1953 Perutz discovered that the isomorphous attachment of heavy atoms to haemoglobin molecules in single crystals produced measurable changes in the diffracted x-ray intensities. This significant discovery showed that it was possible in principle to determine the structure of a globular protein. Application of the same method to myoglobin by Kendrew and his co-workers (1957) resulted in the first three dimensional structure determination of a protein molecule. One of the interesting features of the structure was the α-helical

1

regions, which gave the first direct evidence for the existence of the Pauling-Corey α-helices in proteins.

In 1953 Watson and Crick proposed the now famous double helix structure for DNA. One of the most significant factors which led to this proposal was the x-ray diffraction studies of DNA by Wilkins. The detailed analysis of the diffraction patterns by Wilkins and his co-workers has since confirmed the basic correctness of the Watson-Crick structure.

X-ray diffraction has also given valuable information about the structure of viruses. The classical studies of tobacco mosaic virus by Bernal and Fankuchen in 1941 have been followed by that of Watson (1954), who showed that the virus particle had helical symmetry; by that of Caspar (1956), who showed that it had a central hole, and by that of Franklin (1956), who determined the position of the RNA in the virus particle. Interest in the structure of small spherical viruses was stimulated by the suggestion of Crick and Watson (1956) that they should have icosahedral symmetry. X-ray diffraction studies of bushy stunt virus by Caspar (1956) gave the first experimental support for this suggestion, closely followed by that of Klug and co-workers (1957) from a study of turnip yellow mosaic virus. The detailed structure determination of virus particles, however, remains as one of the most formidable challenges at present confronting x-ray crystallography.

1 Basic Concepts

The aim of this chapter is to discuss briefly some of the basic concepts that are relevant to considerations of molecular structures, and which are used in their description.

1 Atomic Structure

Atoms are about 10^{-8} cm in diameter and consist of a positively charged nucleus surrounded by a number of electrons. Most of the mass of the atom is concentrated in the nucleus, which is about 10^{-13} cm in diameter and is composed of protons and neutrons. Protons have a positive charge numerically equal to that of the electron, but neutrons have no charge. Atoms are electrically neutral so that the number of electrons surrounding the nucleus is equal to the number of protons in the nucleus, and this number, the atomic number of the element, represents its position in the periodic table.

The chemical activity of an element depends on the electronic structure of its atoms. The modern theory of the electronic structure of atoms has developed from the Bohr theory which pictured electrons as occupying fixed orbits of definite energy surrounding the nucleus. With the development of quantum mechanics the orbits of the Bohr model were replaced by orbitals, whose shape represented the probability of finding an electron with a particular energy. Orbitals are characterised by two quantum numbers, and in order of increasing energy they are represented as $1s$, $2s$, $2p$, $3s$, $3p$, $4s$, $3d$, $4p$, $5s$, $4d$, $5p$, $6s$, . . . The numbers represent one quantum number and the small letters represent the other quantum number, where s, p, d, correspond to the numerical values 1, 2, 3 respectively.

The s orbitals are spherically symmetrical but the others are of complicated shapes. The p orbitals, for example, are elongated along three perpendicular axes as shown in Fig. 1.1, and can be represented as p_x, p_y and p_z. An electron can be represented as either spinning in a clockwise or an anti-clockwise direction and according to the Pauli exclusion principle only one electron of a given spin can exist in a given orbital. Thus, in the s orbitals there can be a maximum of two electrons and in the p orbitals a maximum of six, two in each of the three orbitals. There are five different d orbitals, so that a maximum of ten electrons can be accommodated in them.

The various elements in the periodic table contain different numbers of electrons and these electrons are distributed among the various orbitals. Orbitals of lower energy are the first to be filled,

Fig. 1.1 Atomic orbitals.

followed by those of higher energy. Particularly stable electronic arrangements are obtained when certain orbitals are filled with electrons. These represent the electronic arrangements in helium, neon, argon, krypton, xenon and radon, elements which are chemically very inert. For other elements the various orbitals are not completely filled with electrons and this is what determines their chemical activity and the kind of bonds that they form.

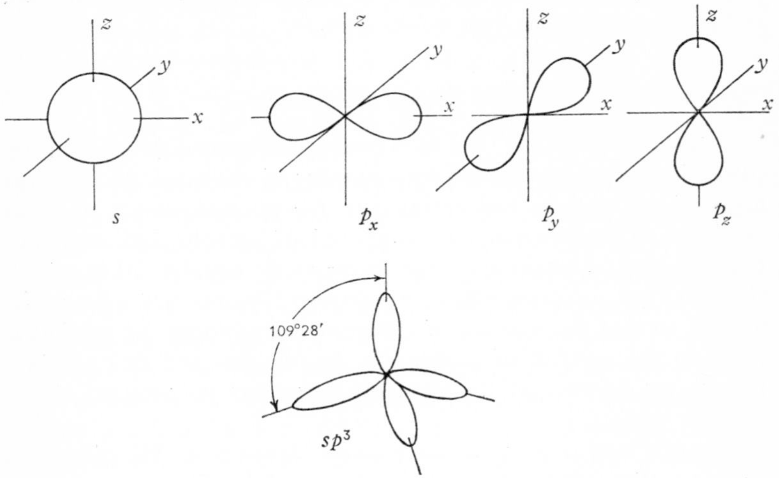

2   Chemical Bonds

a   Ionic bonds

One method of forming a bond between two atoms is by means of electron transfer. If an atom gains or loses an electron it is no longer electrically neutral and it is then called an ion. If one atom gains an electron at the expense of another atom then an electro-static attraction will exist between the two ions. This is referred to as an ionic bond. One example of a structure held together by ionic bonds is a sodium chloride crystal, where the sodium ion is positively charged and the chlorine ion is negatively charged. The transfer of one electron from the sodium atom to the chlorine atom results in each ion attaining the stable electronic configuration of the rare gases—the sodium ion attains the helium arrangement and the chlorine ion that of argon. In order to represent the ionic nature of sodium chloride, its structure is represented as Na^+Cl^-. Ionic bonds have no directional characteristics.

b   Covalent bonds

An alternative method of attaining a stable electronic arrangement is by electron sharing. The atoms which share electrons are attracted to each other and a covalent bond is formed between them. The atomic orbitals of two atoms which are covalently bonded interact and a molecular orbital is formed which may be pictured as an overlap of the atomic orbitals. Thus, two hydrogen atoms attain stable electronic arrangements when they share their two electrons and a molecular orbital is formed by overlap of the atomic orbitals.

A covalent bond which is formed by the sharing of a pair of electrons is called a single bond. When more than one electron is required to give a stable electronic configuration, then more than one single bond can be formed, or else a double bond involving two pairs of electrons, or even a triple bond involving three pairs of electrons.

When a covalent bond is formed between different types of atoms, the shared electrons may be attracted more to one atom than to the other. This gives rise to a separation of charges along the bond, which thus acquires polar characteristics. The more an atom attracts electrons, the more electronegative it is said to be.

The fact that most atomic orbitals are not spherically symmetric and that they overlap in the formation of covalent bonds explains why covalent bonds have directional characteristics. In addition to the directions accounted for by the atomic orbitals referred to already, other directions are explained in terms of the hybridization of atomic orbitals, a process whereby different atomic orbitals blend together to form hybrid orbitals. An example of this effect is the hybridization of the $2s$ and $2p$ orbitals in carbon, which result in four hybrid sp^3 orbitals tetrahedrally arranged around the carbon atom.

c Hydrogen bonds

A hydrogen bond is formed when a hydrogen atom which is covalently bonded to one atom is also attracted to another atom. The two atoms are thus linked together through the hydrogen atom.

Hydrogen bonds are formed between highly electronegative atoms such as fluorine, oxygen and nitrogen. When one of these atoms is covalently bonded to a hydrogen atom, a polar group is formed because the electrons are partly drawn away from the hydrogen atom, leaving it with a positive charge. The hydrogen atom will thus be attracted towards the negative region of an adjacent electro-negative atom. In biological molecules, polar —NH and —OH groups occur very often, and partake in hydrogen bond formation. In contrast to these, non-polar—CH groups do not. Although the strength of a hydrogen bond is less than one-tenth that of a covalent bond, hydrogen bonds play a very important part in determining the conformation of biological molecules, both by intra- and inter-molecular bond formation, and also by the formation of hydrogen bonds between polar groups and water molecules.

A hydrogen bond is represented by a continuous line for the covalent bond to the hydrogen atom and a dotted line to the second atom. Thus, for example, a hydrogen bond between a nitrogen and an oxygen atom is represented as

$$\begin{array}{c} \diagdown \qquad\qquad\qquad \diagup \\ N-H\ldots.O{=}C \\ \diagup \qquad\qquad\qquad \diagdown \end{array}$$

The length of a hydrogen bond is the distance between the non-hydrogen atoms and the values are about 2·8–3·0 Å.

3   Bond Lengths

From the results of x-ray diffraction, electron diffraction and spectroscopic studies, a large amount of information has been obtained about interatomic distances. These results have enabled covalent bond radii to be determined, from which the length of covalent bonds between atoms can be predicted with a fair degree of accuracy.

Deviations from the predicted values may arise due to partial ionic characteristics when bonds are formed between different atoms, but corrections can be applied in such cases. Other deviations which occur in some structures are explained in terms of resonance due to more than one possible electronic configuration in a molecule. Thus in the benzene molecule the C—C bond lengths are 1·39 Å, a value which lies between the single bond value of 1·544 Å and the double bond value of 1·334 Å, and the structure of benzene is the result of resonance between the two Kekule structures

This leads to a definition of the bond order of a covalent bond, which is intermediate between that of a single and a double bond, and which will depend on the number of possible electronic configurations. The resultant structure is more stable than the individual structures and the extra stability is said to be due to resonance energy.

A second example is the C—N bond length in the peptide bond which occurs in protein molecules. This is found to be 1·32 Å whereas the C=N bond is 1·28 Å and a C—N bond is 1·48 Å. This suggests that there is resonance between the two structures:

$$
\begin{array}{ccc}
\underset{\underset{\displaystyle N}{|}}{\overset{\displaystyle O}{\underset{\displaystyle C}{\|}}} & \text{and} & \underset{\underset{\displaystyle N}{|}}{\overset{\displaystyle O^-}{\underset{\displaystyle C}{|}}} \\
| & & | \\
H & & H
\end{array}
$$

4 Bond Angles

The directional characteristics of covalent bonds can be explained in terms of the directions of the atomic orbitals. The p orbitals, for example, are mutually perpendicular so that bonds formed by p orbital overlap would be expected to be at right angles to each other. Sulphur atoms form bonds by means of p orbitals and the angle between the SH bonds in H_2S is 92°. Deviations from the expected values can occur if the bonds have partial ionic characteristics because the bonded atoms can then repel each other. Thus, in H_2O, where the bonds are formed by p orbitals of the oxygen atom, the angle between the OH bonds is increased to 105° because of the repulsion between the hydrogen atoms. When molecules pack together in a crystal, steric hindrance between molecules, or between different parts of a molecule, may also produce changes of a few degrees in bond angles.

Other deviations from the directions expected from the atomic orbital directions can be described in terms of hybridization. Thus the tetrahedral arrangement of the CH bonds in methane is explained in terms of the hybridization of the three $2p$ orbitals and the single $2s$ orbital of carbon to form four sp^3 orbitals which are tetrahedrally arranged about the carbon atom.

When carbon-carbon double bonds are formed it is suggested that hybridization of the $2s$ and two $2p$ orbitals occur, giving rise to three sp^2 hybrid orbitals which are coplanar and at 120° to each other. In the case of carbon-carbon triple bonds the hybridization is believed to be due to the $2s$ and one $2p$ orbital, forming two sp^1 hybrid orbitals which are colinear.

5   Van der Waals Radii

When atoms of different molecules, or of different parts of the same molecule, are close to each other but do not form covalent bonds, they exert weak attractive forces on each other. These are

Table 1   Covalent bond radii and van der Waals radii in Angströms
(1 Angström unit (Å) = 10^{-8} cm)

Element	Single-bond radius	Double-bond radius	Van der Waals radius
Hydrogen	0·30		1·2
Carbon	0·77	0·665	1·7
Nitrogen	0·70	0·60	1·5
Oxygen	0·66	0·55	1·4
Phosphorus	1·10	1·00	1·9

called van der Waals forces. When non-bonded atoms are 'in contact' with each other they are in equilibrium positions where the attractive van der Waals forces are balanced by the repulsive forces due to the interpenetration of the outer orbitals of the atoms. The closest distance of approach of non-bonded atoms can be defined in terms of the van der Waals radii of atoms. Thus, in a space filling model of a molecule the atoms are represented by spheres, or parts of spheres, whose radii are proportional to the van der Waals radii.

6 Rotation About Single Bonds

The large number of possible conformations of a molecule is due to the free rotation which can occur about single bonds. The

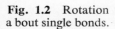
Fig. 1.2 Rotation about single bonds.

restrictions which determine the relative orientations of two groups of atoms that are linked together by a single bond is the interatomic distances between the atoms of the two groups.

7 Molecular Asymmetry

Many compounds are able to rotate the plane of polarization of plane-polarized light. If the rotation is clockwise the compound is said to be *dextro*rotatory and if it is anti-clockwise it is said to be *laevo*rotatory. Such compounds are said to be optically active. Optical activity is due to the asymmetric structure of the molecules of the compound.

If we consider a carbon atom with four different groups tetrahedrally arranged about it, then such an arrangement can not be superimposed on its mirror image, and it is said to be asymmetric. Molecules which contain asymmetric atoms are themselves usually asymmetric and are optically active. Two asymmetric molecules which are mirror images of each other are said to be enantiomorphous and they rotate the plane of polarization in opposite directions.

All amino acids except glycine are asymmetric structures and can

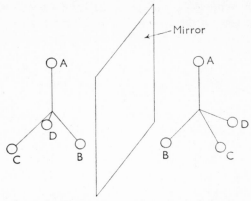

Fig. 1.3 Diagrammatic illustration of enantiomorphous molecules.

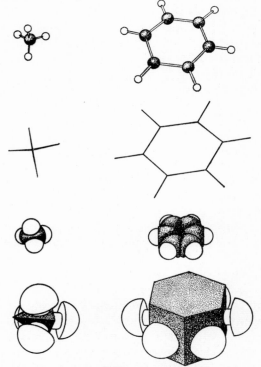

Fig. 1.4 Various types of molecular models representing
methane (CH_4) and benzene (C_6H_6).

exist in enantiomorphous configurations, referred to as the D- and L-configurations. Of these two, only the L-form occurs in proteins. Similarly, in nucleic acids, the configuration of the asymmetric sugar groups is only of one kind.

8 Molecular Models

In the case of fibrous protein and nucleic acid structure analysis, the use of accurate molecular models proved to be of great importance in determining the correct structures. Three types of models are useful in such studies. The first type is a stick-and-ball model, with pieces of stiff metal representing interatomic distances and small coloured balls representing the various atoms. The second type of model, which is used when accurate atomic co-ordinates have to be determined from a molecular model, is built from thin stiff wires welded together and which have freedom of rotation about single bonds. The third type of model is a space-filling model in which the atoms are represented by spheres or parts of spheres whose radii are proportional to the van der Waals radii. The spheres are linked together so that rotation about single bonds and also a certain amount of bond deformation is possible.

2 Crystal Structure
and X-ray Diffraction

1 Crystal Lattice

A crystal consists of a regularly repeating arrangement of atoms or molecules. If we consider any point within the crystal, then there are other points throughout the crystal that are in identical environments. This arrangement of points constitutes a lattice which is referred to as the crystal lattice. The crystal lattice can be defined by three translations, a, b and c, along three axes which are inclined to each other at angles α, β and γ. The small unit of volume of the lattice, with sides equal to a, b and c is called the unit cell. Although the space lattice for a particular crystal is fixed, the axes relating the lattice points, and hence the unit cell, may be chosen in different ways. The most general shape of the unit cell is that of a parallelepiped, but as the symmetry of the lattice increases so the shape of the unit cell becomes simpler. There are seven different shapes for

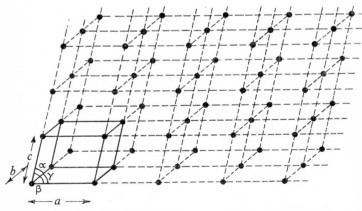

Fig. 2.1 A diagram representing a crystal lattice.
One unit cell is outlined with a continuous line.

Table 2 The seven crystal systems

System	Unit cell dimensions	Minimum essential symmetry
Triclinic	$a \neq b \neq c$ $\alpha \neq \beta \neq \gamma \neq 90°$	None or centre of symmetry
Monoclinic	$a \neq b \neq c$ $\alpha = \gamma = 90°, \beta \neq 90°$	One two-fold axis of rotation or inversion parallel to b
Orthorhombic	$a \neq b \neq c$ $\alpha = \beta = \gamma = 90°$	Three mutually perpendicular two-fold axes of rotation or inversion parallel to a, b and c
Tetragonal	$a = b \neq c$ $\alpha = \beta = \gamma = 90°$	One four-fold axis of rotation or inversion parallel to c
Hexagonal	$a = b \neq c$ $\alpha = \beta = 90°, \gamma = 120°$	One six-fold axis of rotation or inversion parallel to c
Trigonal or Rhombohedral	$a = b = c$ $\alpha = \beta = \gamma < 120° \neq 90°$	One three-fold axis of rotation or inversion parallel to diagonal of the cell
Cubic	$a = b = c$ $\alpha = \beta = \gamma = 90°$	Four three-fold axes parallel to the diagonals of the cell

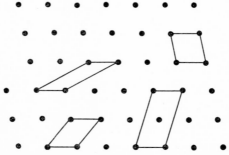

Fig. 2.2 A diagram, showing how different unit cells can be defined for the same lattice. In practice, the choice of unit cell is governed by symmetry considerations.

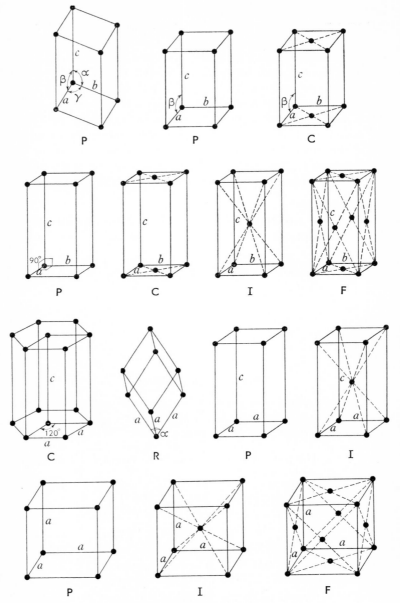

Fig. 2.3 The Bravais Lattices.

unit cells corresponding to different symmetries. These are listed in Table 2.

When there are lattice points only at each corner of the unit cell, the unit cell contains one basic unit of structure, which, when repeated regularly will build up the crystal. The unit cell is then said to be primitive and is represented by the symbol *P*. In some cases it is more appropriate to consider a unit cell which contains more than one unit of structure. Thus, for example, some cubic lattices have a body-centred unit cell which contains two structure units, and others have a face-centred unit cell which contains four structure units. The total number of primitive and non-primitive lattices is fourteen, and these are referred to as the Bravais lattices.

a   Lattice planes

The crystal lattice points lie on sets of equidistant parallel planes. These sets of planes were shown by W. L. Bragg (1912) to provide

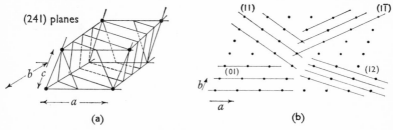

Fig. 2.4   Lattice planes.

a basis for a simple interpretation of x-ray diffraction by a crystal. A particular set of planes is characterized by three indices *h*, *k* and *l*, where the intercepts of the planes along the axes of the crystal lattice are $\frac{a}{h}, \frac{b}{k}, \frac{c}{l}$. The indices may be positive or negative depending on whether the intercept is on the positive or negative direction of the axis. Negative indices are written as $\bar{h}$, $\bar{k}$ and $\bar{l}$.

2   Symmetry

An object possesses symmetry if it is possible to operate on it in such a way that it retains its original appearance. The operations which can do this are called symmetry operations. Thus, for example, if a cube is rotated through an angle of 90° about an axis through the centre of opposite faces, the cube retains its original appearance because it has been rotated into self coincidence. The symmetry operation in this case is one of rotation, and the axis of rotation is a four-fold axis. In general, an object possesses an *n*-fold axis of ro-

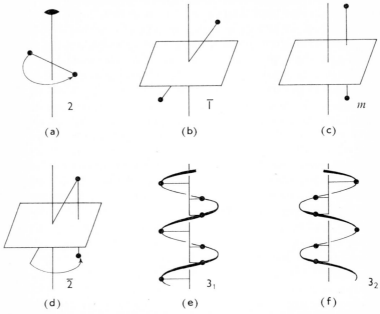

Fig. 2.5 Symmetry operations (a) two-fold rotation, (b) inversion, (c) reflection, (d) two-fold inversion, (e) 3_1 and 3_2 screw.

tation if it is brought into self-coincidence when it is rotated through an angle of $360°/n$ about that axis.

For an isolated object there is no restriction on the value of *n*, but for a crystal lattice the values of *n* are restricted to 1, 2, 3, 4 and 6 because the lattice must be space filling. When the rotational symmetries of crystals are investigated it is found that they can be grouped into seven divisions, called the seven crystal systems.

Other symmetry operations are those of reflection and inversion. Reflection symmetry is represented by the symbol *m* and that of inversion by $\bar{1}$. An object which possesses a centre of inversion is said to be centro-symmetric. If rotation symmetry is combined with inversion it gives rise to inversion axes which are represented by the symbols $\bar{1}, \bar{2}, \bar{3}, \bar{4}$ and $\bar{6}$. The operations $\bar{2}$ and *m* are thus equivalent. (See Fig. 2.5.)

The set of symmetry operations that can be performed on an object constitute a point group. There are 32 point groups which apply to crystals and they give rise to the 32 crystal classes which are distributed through the seven crystal systems. The external symmetry of crystals is thus limited to the 32 crystal classes.

If, however, the internal structure of a crystal is taken into account, then additional symmetry elements are possible because the crystal repeats regularly in three dimensions. The additional symmetry elements are the screw axis and the glide plane. A screw axis combines rotation with translation, and a glide plane combines reflection with translation. A screw axis is represented as n_p, where the rotation is $360°/n$ and the translation is a fraction p/n of the lattice translation along that axis. Thus a 2_1 axis parallel to the b-axis represents a rotation of $180°$ and a translation of $b/2$, and is referred to as a two-fold screw axis. In the case of a three-fold screw axis there are two possible arrangements, depending on whether the screw axis is right- or left-handed. These are written as 3_1 and 3_2 respectively. Similar considerations apply to four-fold and six-fold screw axes, where 4_1 and 4_3, and 6_1 and 6_5 axes are mirror images of each other.

The addition of glide planes and screw axes to rotation and inversion axes increases the possible combination of symmetry elements to 230, and these are called the 230 space groups. Each space group can be represented by a set of symbols, the most common system being the Herman-Mauguin notation. The first symbol in the space group notation is a capital letter to indicate the type of Bravais lattice. This is followed by the minimum symmetry elements of the space group. Thus $P2_1$ represents a primitive cell with a two-fold screw axis, while $C2$ represents a lattice centred on the ab faces, with a two-fold rotation axis. The space group $P2_1/c$ contains a combination of a two-fold screw axis and a glide plane parallel to the c-axis, a combination which gives rise also to a centre of symmetry although this is not included in the space group notation.

Full details of the distribution of symmetry elements for the different space groups are given in Volume I of the International Tables for X-ray Crystallography (Kynoch Press, Birmingham).

If we consider an asymmetric group of atoms which are in general positions in the unit cell, then the symmetry operations give rise to other groups of atoms which are in equivalent general positions. The number of equivalent general positions which are related by the symmetry operations represent the number of asymmetric units within the unit cell. The number of asymmetric units is related to the number of molecules in the unit cell, and if these are equal, or if there is more than one molecule in the asymmetric unit, then no direct information is obtained about the symmetry of the molecule. If, however, there is a smaller number of molecules than there are asymmetric units, then the molecules must occupy special positions in the cell and the molecule must possess the appropriate symmetry element of the space group. Thus, for example, in one form of horse haemoglobin which crystallizes in the space group C2, the number of molecules per asymmetric unit is one-half so that the molecule itself must contain a two-fold axis.

a   Space group determination

If the space group of a crystal is known, it means that the number of asymmetric units in the unit cell is known. This information will indicate the fraction of the unit cell that has to be investigated, and in some cases can give information about the molecules themselves.

Symmetry operations give rise to systematic absences of spectra in the x-ray diffraction patterns, so that an examination of the missing spectra is a necessary step in space group determination. Systematic absences may not enable the space group to be determined uniquely, and other methods, such as the statistical analysis of intensities, have to be used. In the case of most biological molecules the problem of space group determination is simplified because the molecules are of a definite handedness due to the presence of asymmetric groups of one kind only. This means that they do not crystallize in space groups containing centres of symmetry, mirror planes or glide planes, and the possible number of space groups is reduced from 230 to 69.

In order to determine the number of molecules in the asymmetric unit of a structure, the density of the crystal should be measured and the molecular weight should be known approximately. If the volume of the unit cell is V cm³ and the density of the crystal is ρ gm cm⁻³, then the product $\rho V = nm$, where n is the number of molecules in the unit cell, and m is the mass, in gm, of one molecule. The mass m is related to the molecular weight M by the equation

$$m = 1 \cdot 660 \times 10^{-24} M$$

so that

$$M = \frac{\rho V \times 10^{24}}{1 \cdot 660 \, n}$$

The number of molecules in the unit cell must be an integer, so that n can be determined if M is known only approximately. Having determined n, a more accurate value of the molecular weight is then obtainable.

3 The Reciprocal Lattice

The concept of the reciprocal lattice is of fundamental importance in x-ray crystallography because it facilitates the interpretation of diffraction patterns.

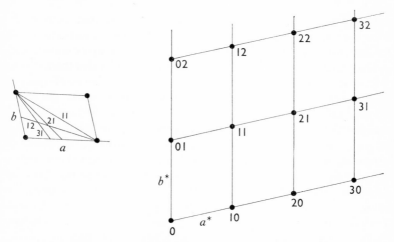

Fig. 2.6 Construction of the reciprocal lattice.

The construction of the reciprocal lattice can be considered by reference to the two-dimensional example in Fig. 2.6. From an origin, points are drawn at distances of $\frac{1}{d}$ parallel to the normals of lattice planes of spacing d. These points constitute the reciprocal lattice. The axes of the reciprocal lattice are represented by the symbols a^*, b^* and c^* and the reciprocal lattice points will have indices hkl.

4 Diffraction of X-rays

X-rays, like visible light, are part of the electromagnetic spectrum of radiation, and differ from visible light only in the magnitude of their wavelengths. Whereas visible light has a wavelength of the order of 5×10^{-5} cm, the wavelengths of x-rays are of the order of 10^{-8} cm or 1 Angström unit (Å).

In modern physics, both radiation and matter are considered to have complementary wave and particle aspects. The results of some experiments can be explained on the basis of a wave theory while those of other experiments are explained in terms of a particle theory. Diffraction of x-rays by matter can be explained in terms of the wave theory of radiation.

X-rays which are incident on a specimen are scattered by the electrons within the atoms of the material, and diffraction effects are due to interference between the scattered radiation from the various atoms. From an analysis of the diffracted x-rays it is theoretically possible to determine the arrangement of the atoms within the material. The reason why it should be possible to do this becomes apparent if we consider Abbe's theory of image formation with a lens. In Abbe's theory, optical image formation is considered to be a two stage process; the first stage, in which light is scattered by the object and gives rise to diffraction effects, and the second stage, when the scattered waves are brought together by the lens to form an image. X-ray diffraction corresponds to the first stage in the Abbe theory, but because there is no suitable material for focusing x-rays, the second stage must be carried out mathematically. There is no reason, however, why this should not be a straight-forward procedure, provided enough information is known about the scattered x-rays.

The resultant scattered radiation from an object in a particular direction is characterised by two quantities, an amplitude term and a phase term, and the distribution of amplitude and phase in different directions, for all possible directions of the incident beam, is called the Fourier transform of the object. The first stage in Abbe's theory is thus said to be a Fourier transformation, and the second stage is called an inverse Fourier transformation. In order to carry out the inverse Fourier transformation mathematically, both the amplitude and phase of the diffracted x-rays must be known. The major difficulty in x-ray structure analysis lies in the fact that only the amplitudes can be directly determined by experiment, so that the main problem is to find methods of determining the phases.

The physical principles underlying x-ray diffraction are clarified by comparison with the diffraction effects observed with visible light (see e.g. Bragg (1939), Preston (1944), Lipson and Cochran (1953), Taylor and Lipson (1964)).

5   Optical Phenomena

a   Abbe's theory of image formation

If a parallel beam of light is incident on an object (Fig. 2.7) scattering occurs in all directions, and some of the light will be collected

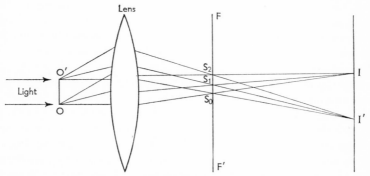

Fig. 2.7   Image formation by a lens.

by the lens. Light that is scattered in a particular direction will be brought together at a particular point in the focal plane of the lens (FF). The interference between the various waves from different parts of the object give rise to a Fraunhofer diffraction pattern in the focal plane. Each point in the focal plane may be considered as a source of coherent secondary waves which interfere with each other to form the final image. The more scattered light that is collected by the lens, the greater will be the extent of the diffraction pattern in the focal plane, and the more detailed the image.

b   Fraunhofer diffraction by a slit and by a diffraction grating

If a beam of parallel, monochromatic light is incident upon a slit situated in front of a lens, then a Fraunhofer diffraction pattern will be observed in the focal plane of the lens. The intensity at any point in the pattern is proportional to the square of the amplitude at that point, and the distribution of amplitude in the pattern is illustrated in Fig. 2.8.

When the single slit is replaced by a diffraction grating consisting of a large number of parallel, identical slits, the distribution of amplitude in the diffraction pattern is related to that of the single

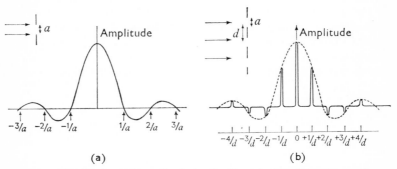

(a)   (b)

Fig. 2.8   Distribution of amplitude in the Fraunhofer diffraction pattern (a) due to a single slit; (b) due to a diffraction grating with apertures of the same width as the single slit.

slit pattern, but is modified due to the interference between the light from different slits. The effect of this interference is to produce a diffraction pattern consisting of discrete spectra rather than the continuous distribution obtained with the single slit. The positions of the spectra depend on the slit separation but their amplitudes depend on the slit width. We can say that because there is a regular arrangement of slits in the grating, the single slit pattern is only 'sampled' at the positions of the spectra.

6   Wave Motion

a   Wave representation

The wave equation representing the propagation of a disturbance, y, along an x-axis may be written as

$$y = a \sin (\omega t - kx) \qquad (1)$$

where a is the amplitude of the wave; t is the time; $\omega = 2\pi/T$, where T is the period of the wave; and $k = 2\pi/\lambda$, where λ is the wavelength.

Fig. 2.9 Two waves of the same wavelength displaced relative to each other.

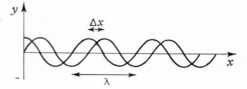

The quantity $(\omega t - kx)$ represents the phase of the wave and is important in relating the positions of the crests and troughs of a wave to those of other waves. For a fixed value of t, a change λ in x produces a phase change of 2π. Hence, if the crests of two waves are displaced by a distance Δx, the phase difference between them will be $\dfrac{2\pi}{\lambda} \cdot \Delta x$.

An alternative representation of wave propagation makes use of complex quantities. Thus, a disturbance y may be written as

$$y = a \exp i(\omega t - kx). \qquad (2)$$

A complex quantity is represented by $z = x + iy$ where $i^2 = -1$. The quantities x and y are called the real and imaginary parts of z, respectively. The complex conjugate of z is written as z^* and is obtained by replacing i by $-i$. Thus, $z^* = x - iy$. The quantity $|z|$ is called the modulus of z, and is the positive value of the square root of $x^2 + y^2$. Hence, $|z| = \sqrt{x^2 + y^2} = \sqrt{zz^*}$. $\qquad (3)$

A complex quantity can be represented by a line in a plane, of length $r(= |z|)$ at an angle θ to the x-axis. Thus $x = r \cos \theta$ and $y = r \sin \theta$.

Hence,
$$z = x + iy$$
$$= r \cos \theta + ir \sin \theta$$
$$= r \exp i\theta \qquad (4)$$

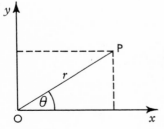

Fig. 2.10 Representation of a complex number in an Argand diagram.

and $$z^* = r \exp(-i\theta). \tag{5}$$

The intensity of a wave is proportional to the square of the amplitude, that is, to a^2. From equation (2)

$$y = a \exp i\omega t \cdot \exp(-kx)$$
$$= P \exp i\omega t, \quad \text{where } P = a \exp(-kx). \tag{6}$$

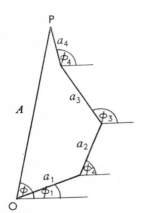

Fig. 2.11   Addition of complex numbers in an Argand diagram.

The intensity is thus proportional to PP^* or $|P|^2$, both of which are equal to a^2.

b   Superposition of waves

Interference effects occur when several waves pass through the same point. The resultant disturbance due to a number of waves is equal to the sum of the individual disturbances. Thus, if the individual disturbances are represented by $y_1, y_2, y_3, \ldots$ the resultant disturbance, y, is given by

$$y = y_1 + y_2 + y_3 + \cdots \qquad = \sum y_j \tag{7}$$

where $y_j = a_j \exp i(\omega t + \phi_j)$,

replacing $-kx$ in equation (2) by ϕ.

Thus, $y = (a_1 \exp i\phi_1 + a_2 \exp i\phi_2 + \cdots) \exp i\omega t$
$$= \exp i\omega t \sum a_j \exp i\phi_j = A \exp i\phi \cdot \exp i\omega t \tag{8}$$

The resultant amplitude and phase thus depend on $\sum a_j \exp i\phi_j$.

7 Reciprocal Space

If we consider a beam of parallel, monochromatic radiation incident upon an object and scattered through an angle 2θ, then the incident and scattered rays can be represented by vectors s_0 and s, both of lengths $\frac{1}{\lambda}$, where λ is the wavelength of the radiation.

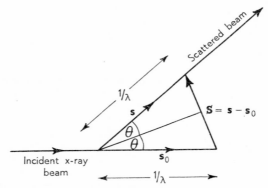

Fig. 2.12   Vector representation of scattering of x-rays.

Representing the lengths of the vectors by $|s_0|$ and $|s|$, then $|s_0| = |s| = \frac{1}{\lambda}$.

We can now define a vector S as the difference between the vectors s and s_0

$$S = s - s_0. \tag{9}$$

Since $|s_0| = |s| = \frac{1}{\lambda}$, it follows from Fig. 2.12 that $|S| = \frac{2 \sin \theta}{\lambda}$.

Hence the dimensions of S are the reciprocal of a length.

The end of the vector S is a point in what is called reciprocal space, and this is the space in which the Fourier transform of the object is described. The measurement of the scattered intensity from an object at a particular angle is a determination of the intensity for a particular value of S, and hence at a particular point in reciprocal space. If the direction of the incident x-ray beam is fixed, then the end of the vector **S** can only lie on the surface of the sphere swept out by the vector **s**. This sphere is called the sphere of reflection, or the Ewald sphere. Thus, for a fixed direction of the incident beam, the intensity can be determined only at points on the surface of the sphere of reflection.

If the direction of the incident beam is changed, then another region of reciprocal space can be investigated, since the new sphere

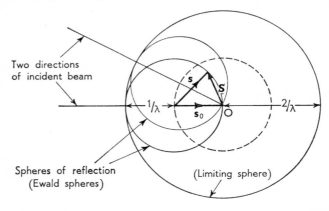

Fig. 2.13 A section of reciprocal space showing the sphere of reflection and the limiting sphere.

of reflection will be displaced relative to the first one. For all possible orientations of the incident beam, the centres of the spheres of reflection fall on the surface of a sphere with centre O (Fig. 2.13) and radius equal to s_0, so that a spherical region of reciprocal space, of radius $2|s_0|$ or $\frac{2}{\lambda}$, can be examined. No information is obtained about the region of reciprocal space outside the sphere of radius $\frac{2}{\lambda}$, and for this reason it is called the limiting sphere.

8 Atomic Scattering of X-rays

Diffraction of x-rays by matter is due to the interference of radiation scattered by the electrons within the atoms. The amplitude of the waves scattered by a particular atom depends on the number of electrons in the atom, and is characterized by the atomic scattering factor, f_0, which is the ratio of the amplitude scattered by the atom to the amplitude scattered by a single electron. The atomic scattering factors depend on the distribution of electrons in the atom and have been calculated theoretically. At zero scattering angle, f_0 is equal to the atomic number of the atom, but because of the finite volume over which the electrons extend, its value decreases as the scattering angle increases. Typical curves showing the variation of scattering factor with scattering angle are shown in Fig. 2.14.

Fig. 2.14 Atomic scattering curves.

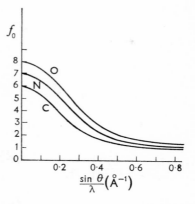

Scattering factors are calculated on the assumption that the atoms are at rest. In practice, however, thermal motion of the atoms occurs and they oscillate about a mean position with a finite amplitude of oscillation. This temperature effect further reduces the scattering factor, so that in practice the factor f is used where

$$f = f_0 \exp\left(-B \sin^2 \frac{\theta}{\lambda}\right) \qquad (10)$$

where B is a constant related to the displacement of the atom due to temperature.

9 Phase Relationships

If we consider a group of atoms in a beam of x-rays, then interference between the scattered radiation from different atoms will depend on the phase relationships between the scattered waves, which in turn depend on the relative positions of the atoms within the group.

When x-rays are scattered by an atom, in general they suffer a phase change of π, but since this is the same for all the atoms, it does not affect the relative phases between the scattered waves.

We consider an atom at A (Fig. 2.15) with its position relative to the origin O defined by the vector $\mathbf{r}$. In order to derive the phase relationships between scattered waves we consider scattering to occur also from the origin O. Thus the phase difference between the

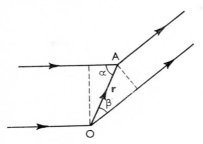

Fig. 2.15   The scattering of x-rays from two points.

waves scattered by O and A will be due to the path difference between the waves, which is $|\mathbf{r}|\,(\cos\beta - \cos\alpha)$. This corresponds to a phase difference of $\dfrac{2\pi}{\lambda}\,|\mathbf{r}|\,(\cos\beta - \cos\alpha)$.

The scalar product of two vectors $\mathbf{a}$ and $\mathbf{b}$ is written as $\mathbf{a}\cdot\mathbf{b}$ and is equal to the product of $|\mathbf{a}|$ and $|\mathbf{b}|$ and the cosine of the angle between them. Since $|\mathbf{s}| = |\mathbf{s}_0| = \dfrac{1}{\lambda}$, then

$$\frac{|\mathbf{r}|\cos\beta}{\lambda} \quad \text{and} \quad \frac{|\mathbf{r}|\cos\alpha}{\lambda}$$

are scalar products and can be written as $\mathbf{r}\cdot\mathbf{s}$ and $\mathbf{r}\cdot\mathbf{s}_0$ respectively. The phase difference, therefore, becomes $2\pi\mathbf{r}\cdot(\mathbf{s}-\mathbf{s}_0) = 2\pi\mathbf{r}\cdot\mathbf{S}$.

10   Diffraction by a Molecule

We consider a molecule, composed of a number of atoms, to be situated in a parallel beam of monochromatic x-rays. Let the positions of the atoms be given by the vectors $\mathbf{r}_1, \mathbf{r}_2, \mathbf{r}_3, \ldots \mathbf{r}_n$, and let the scattering factors for these atoms be $f_1, f_2, f_3 \ldots f_n$, respectively. The resultant disturbance in a particular direction is then given by

$$G(\mathbf{S}) = \sum f_j \exp\left(2\pi i \mathbf{r}_j \cdot \mathbf{S}\right) \tag{11}$$

This equation can be written in a more general form by replacing the f's by the electron density in the molecule, represented by $\rho(\mathbf{r})$. The equation then becomes

$$G(\mathbf{S}) = \int \rho(\mathbf{r}) \exp{(2\pi i \mathbf{r} \cdot \mathbf{S})} \, dv_\mathbf{r} \tag{12}$$

the integral being over all the volume for which the electron density is finite.

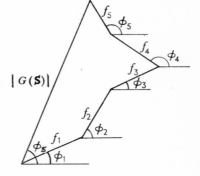

Fig. 2.16 Graphical determination of the resultant scattering from a molecule.

In general, $G(\mathbf{S})$ is a complex quantity and can be expressed as

$$G(\mathbf{S}) = |G(\mathbf{S})| \exp{(i\alpha_\mathbf{s})} \tag{13}$$

but if the molecule has a centre of symmetry $G(\mathbf{S})$ is a real quantity and then

$$G(\mathbf{S}) = \pm |G(\mathbf{S})| \tag{14}$$

Two functions which are related as $G(\mathbf{S})$ and $\rho(\mathbf{r})$ are related in equation (12) are said to be Fourier transform pairs, and because of this we can write

$$\rho(r) = \int G(\mathbf{S}) \exp{(-2\pi i \mathbf{r} \cdot \mathbf{S})} \, dv_\mathbf{s} \tag{15}$$

where the integration is now made over reciprocal space.

Using this formula, it should, therefore, be possible to determine the electron density distribution in the molecule and hence determine its structure. The difficulty, however, is that only the amplitude of $G(\mathbf{S})$ can be directly determined by experiment since the measured intensity $I(\mathbf{S})$ is proportional to $|G(\mathbf{S})|^2$. Hence, before a direct structure analysis can be carried out, information about the phases must be obtained.

In general, $I(\mathbf{S}) = I(-\mathbf{S})$ so that the intensity distribution has a centre of symmetry at the origin of reciprocal space, although the scattering object itself may be non-centrosymmetrical. However, if the incident x-rays have a frequency close to an absorption frequency of the scattering atoms, $I(\mathbf{S}) \neq I(-\mathbf{S})$.

11   Diffraction by a Crystal

A crystal consists of a regular arrangement of atoms or molecules, and the basic unit which repeats throughout the crystal is the contents of the unit cell. If we consider diffraction from the contents of a single unit cell, then its Fourier transform, in general, will be continuous throughout reciprocal space. However, the effect of having a large number of regularly arranged unit cells is to confine the diffraction to discrete regions, so that the transform is only finite at particular points, these being the points of the reciprocal lattice. We can then say that in the case of diffraction by a crystal the Fourier transform of the unit cell contents is 'sampled' at the reciprocal lattice points. The values of the Fourier transform at the reciprocal lattice points are called structure factors, and are denoted as $F(hkl)$.

The manner in which the diffraction by a crystal is limited to reciprocal lattice points is analogous to the limitation of diffracted light into spectra in the case of diffraction by a grating. A crystal, because of its regularity, behaves as a three-dimensional grating.

a   Laue's equations

The conditions which obtain for diffraction by a three-dimensional crystal lattice were first derived by Laue (1912). Let us consider an x-ray beam incident at an angle α_0 on a single row of lattice points of spacing a (Fig. 2.17). For a diffracted beam at an angle α, the condition for constructive interference is that the path difference between successive waves should be an integral number of wavelengths, i.e. $a(\cos\alpha - \cos\alpha_0) = h\lambda$ where h is an integer.

Using the vector notation, this equation can be written as $\mathbf{a} \cdot \mathbf{S} = h$, because $|\mathbf{s}| = |\mathbf{s}_0| = \dfrac{1}{\lambda}$, and $\mathbf{S} = \mathbf{s} - \mathbf{s}_0$.

If the lattice points along the other two axes, of spacings b and c respectively, are considered in turn, then two further conditions are obtained, namely,

$$\mathbf{b} \cdot \mathbf{S} = k$$

and

$$\mathbf{c} \cdot \mathbf{S} = l \tag{16}$$

These three equations constitute the Laue equations, and for diffraction from a crystal lattice, the three equations must be

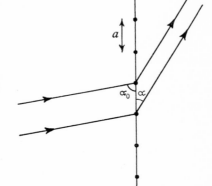

Fig. 2.17 Diffraction by a single row of lattice points.

satisfied simultaneously. Each Laue equation defines a set of parallel, equidistant planes in reciprocal space, and the intersections of these planes form the reciprocal lattice, since only at the intersections are the three equations satisfied simultaneously.

If a crystal is rotated about one of the space lattice axes (the a-axis, say) and the x-ray beam is incident at right angles to this axis, then α_0 is zero in the first Laue equation so that

$$a \cos \alpha = h\lambda \tag{17}$$

When $h = 1, 2, 3, \ldots$, the diffracted spectra lie on a set of cones with semi-vertical angles, $\alpha_1, \alpha_2, \alpha_3 \ldots$. These cones will intersect a cylindrical film surrounding the crystal in a series of straight lines called layer lines (Fig. 2.19). The angle α can be determined experimentally by measuring the separation of the zeroth and the hth layer line on the film, y, and also the distance between the crystal and the film, x. The angle α is then obtained from the equation

$$\tan (90° - \alpha) = \frac{y}{x} \tag{18}$$

Hence, the axial length, a, can be calculated. From rotation photographs about the other two axes, b and c can be determined.

b Bragg's equation

A simpler interpretation of diffraction by a crystal was made by W. L. Bragg (1913), who considered the diffracted beams as arising by reflection of x-rays from lattice planes. If the x-ray beam is

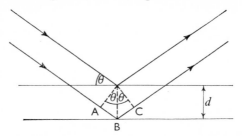

Fig. 2.18   Bragg reflection from lattice planes.

incident on lattice planes of spacing d, then for a particular angle of incident θ, the scattered x-rays reinforce so that the x-rays can be considered to be 'reflected' off the lattice planes. The path difference between the beams reflected from successive planes (Fig. 2.18) is $AB + BC = 2d \sin \theta$, which, for constructive interference must be an integral number of wavelengths. Hence

$$2d \sin \theta = n\lambda. \tag{19}$$

This is known as the Bragg equation. From the conditions laid down by this equation we see that only if a lattice plane is at the correct orientation relative to the incident x-ray beam will reflection occur. From our earlier considerations, for a stationary object and a fixed incident beam, the sampled region of reciprocal space lies on the surface of the Ewald sphere. Hence, when the Bragg equation is satisfied for a set of planes, the corresponding reciprocal lattice point must then lie on the Ewald sphere. The two ways of looking at the condition for observing a diffracted spectrum are equivalent, one referring to the space lattice and the other to the reciprocal lattice.

c Structure factors

The structure factors are the values of the Fourier transform of the unit cell contents at the reciprocal lattice points. The Fourier

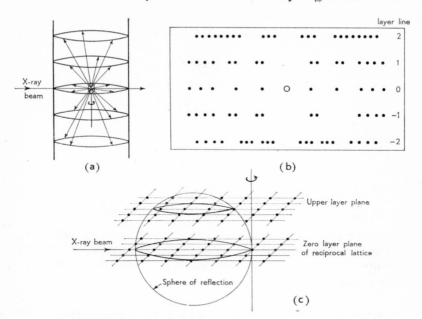

Fig. 2.19 Rotation photograph from a single crystal.

(a) Rotating crystal with cylindrical film around it.

(b) Diagram showing the appearance of the diffraction pattern on the opened out film.

(c) Rotation photograph from the reciprocal lattice point of view. As the reciprocal lattice rotates the lattice points pass through the sphere of reflection and hence satisfy the diffraction condition.

transform of the atoms in the unit cell is given by

$$G(\mathbf{S}) = \sum_{j=1}^{n} f_j \exp 2\pi i \mathbf{r}_j \cdot \mathbf{S} \qquad (20)$$

where $\mathbf{r}_j$ is the vector representing the position of the jth atom, and can be written as

$$\mathbf{r}_j = x_j\mathbf{a} + y_j\mathbf{b} + z_j\mathbf{c} \qquad (21)$$

where x_j, y_j, z_j are the fractional co-ordinates of the atoms.

Substituting for $\mathbf{r}_j$ in equation (20), and applying the Laue equations, we obtain

$$F(hkl) = \sum_{j=1}^{n} f_j \exp \left[2\pi i (hx_j + ky_j + lz_j)\right] \qquad (22)$$

The structure factors are complex quantities and the real and imaginary parts can be represented by $A(hkl)$ and $B(hkl)$ respectively, where

$$A(hkl) = \sum f_j \cos [2\pi(hx_j + ky_j + lz_j)]$$

$$B(hkl) = \sum f_j \sin [2\pi(hx_j + ky_j + lz_j)]$$

Hence $$|F(hkl)| = \sqrt{A^2 + B^2}. \tag{23}$$

Alternatively, we may write

$$F(hkl) = |F(hkl)| \exp i\alpha(hkl) \tag{24}$$

where $\alpha(hkl) = \tan^{-1}B(hkl)/A(hkl)$

d   Representation of electron density by a Fourier series

Rather than consider discrete atoms with scattering factors f_j, we can consider a function $\rho(xyz)$ which represents the electron density at a point within the cell with fractional co-ordinates (xyz). Thus, equation (22) can be written as

$$F(hkl) = V \int \int \int \rho(xyz) \exp [2\pi i(hx + ky + lz)] \, dx \, dy \, dz \tag{25}$$

where the integration is over the unit cell of volume V.

Because a crystal is a regular structure, the electron density can be represented by a Fourier series and we can write

$$\rho(xyz) = \frac{1}{V} \sum_h \sum_k \sum_l F(hkl) \exp [-2\pi i(hx + ky + lz)]. \tag{26}$$

Often in single crystal analysis a projection of the structure on to a plane is determined first. If a projection down the c-axis of the unit cell is required, then the electron density distribution is given by

$$\rho(xy) = \frac{1}{A} \sum_h \sum_k F(hkO) \exp [-2\pi i(hx + ky)] \tag{27}$$

where A is the area of the plane.

Equation (26) is not in a form which makes it easy to calculate the electron density distribution because it contains complex quantities. By suitable substitution it can be rewritten as

$$\rho(xyz) = \frac{1}{V} \sum \sum \sum |F(hkl)| \cos [2\pi(hx + ky + lz) - \alpha(hkl)] \tag{28}$$

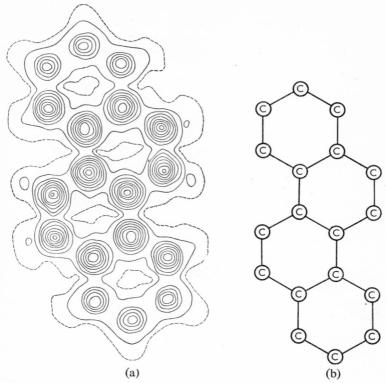

(a)   (b)

Fig. 2.20 (a) Section of a three-dimensional Fourier synthesis in the plane of a chrysene molecule. Controus representing the electron density are drawn at intervals of 1 electron/Å^3 (from Burns and Iball, 1960). (b) Diagram of the atoms in (a).

where $F(hkl)$ is the amplitude of the structure factor and $\alpha(hkl)$ is the phase.

12 Diffraction by Fibres

Many naturally occurring biological structures are of a fibrous nature, and, in addition, other biological molecules can be oriented into fibres when isolated from living cells. X-ray diffraction patterns are usually obtained by placing the fibres at right angles to the x-ray beam. The direction parallel to the fibre axis and through the centre of a fibre diffraction pattern is referred to as the meridian, and the direction perpendicular to this is called the equator.

Fibres are usually composed of long, chain-like molecules, packed together with their axes parallel, or nearly parallel, to the fibre axis. Apart from the common axial direction, however, the degree of order within fibres may vary considerably. In some fibres the

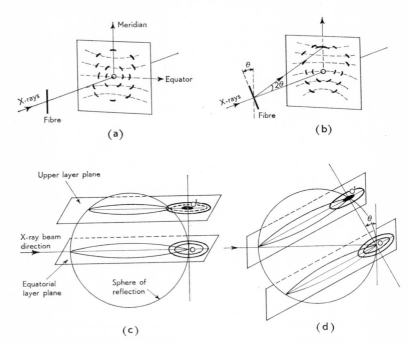

Fig. 2.21   Diffraction by a fibre.
    (a) Fibre perpendicular to the x-ray beam.
    (b) Fibre tilted at the appropriate angle to record a meridional reflection.
    (c) Diagram of the reciprocal lattice when the fibre axis is perpendicular to the x-ray beam, and showing that no information is obtained about the region around O′ which does not intersect the sphere of reflection.
    (d) Diagram showing the reciprocal lattice tilted so that O′ falls on the reflecting sphere.

molecules are regularly arranged so as to form crystalline regions, but the different crystalline regions within a fibre are randomly oriented about the fibre axis. The diffraction patterns from such fibres are similar to single crystal rotation photographs, although spots may be drawn out into arcs due to disorientation, and may be rather broad if the crystalline regions are small.

In other fibres the degree of order is very much less, and various kinds of disorder give rise to characteristic diffraction effects. If molecules are randomly displaced relative to each other in the direction of the fibre axis, discrete spots are only observed along the equator, and the higher layer lines have a continuous distribution of intensity along them. A random displacement by a fixed amount

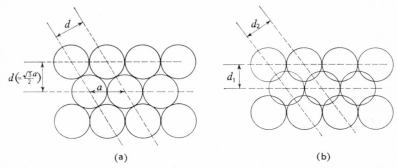

(a) (b)

Fig. 2.22 A projection down a fibre axis showing commonly occurring close-packing arrangements of helical molecules (a) hexagonal arrangement, (b) deviation from hexagonal due to different amount of interpretation of molecules in various directions.

can give rise to discrete spots on some layer lines and a continuous streak of intensity along others. Thus, a random displacement by half the repeat period along the fibre axis will produce spots on the even numbered layer lines and streaks on the odd ones.

Screw disorder, which is a combination of rotational and translational disorder, is common with helical molecules. This gives rise to diffraction patterns with discrete spots in the central region but continuous streaks elsewhere along the layer lines.

Discrete spots along the meridian indicate periodicities along the fibre axis. In order to obtain information about the regions of the transform near the origins of the higher layer planes it is necessary to tilt the fibre through half the scattering angle for that region.

The diffraction along the equator of the pattern gives information about the structure in projection down the fibre axis, and even if the rest of the diffraction pattern is rather diffuse, discrete spots along the equator will indicate the lateral distance between molecules.

13 Diffraction by Helical Molecules

The theory of diffraction by a helical molecule has played an important part in determining the conformation of many biological molecules. It was first developed by Cochran, Crick and Vand (1952), and by Stokes (unpublished).

a The Fourier transform of a continuous helix

Following the procedure of Cochran, Crick and Vand, let us first consider the transform of a uniform, continuous helix of negligible

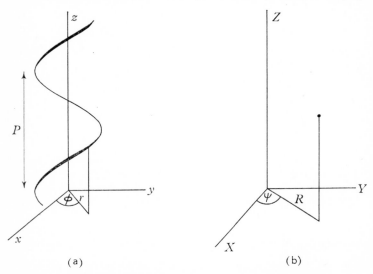

(a)   (b)

Fig. 2.23 (a) A uniform helix of pitch P and radius r.
(b) The co-ordinate system in reciprocal space.

thickness, of radius r and pitch, P. A point on the helix is represented by cylindrical co-ordinates (r, ϕ, z) and a point in reciprocal space is represented by (R, ψ, Z).

Since P is the repeat distance along the helix, the Fourier transform is confined to layer planes of spacing $\dfrac{1}{P}$, and the diffraction pattern would have layer lines with spacing proportional to this. The Fourier transform on the lth layer plane is given by

$$G(R, \psi, l/P) = J_l(2\pi Rr) \exp il(\psi + \pi/2) \qquad (29)$$

where J_l is a Bessel function of the lth order.

Bessel functions enter into the equation because a cylindrical co-ordinate system is used. The variation of $J_l(X)$ with l and X is illustrated in Fig. 2.24. It is noticeable that only the zero order Bessel function, $J_0(X)$, has non-zero value at $X = 0$. It is also noticeable that the value of $J_l(X)$ for the first maximum decreases as l increases, and that the first maximum occurs at increasing values of X as l increases.

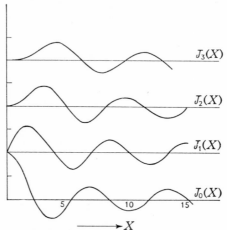

Fig. 2.24   Bessel functions.

The intensity distribution on the lth layer plane is proportional to $\left| G\left(R, \psi, \dfrac{l}{P} \right) \right|^2$ and hence to $|J_l(2\pi Rr)|^2$, which is independent of ψ.

Because the first maximum of Bessel functions move further away from the origin as the order increases, the centre of the diffraction pattern would have a cross-like appearance. The steeper the helix, the larger the angle between the arms of the cross and the meridian. As the zero order Bessel function only contributes to the equator, there would be no diffracted intensity along the meridian.

b   The Fourier transform of a discontinuous helix

A discontinuous helix can be considered as a set of scattering points, equally spaced along a helix. Let the vertical distance between such points be p, and let the pitch of the helix be P. The number of points per turn of the helix is thus $\dfrac{P}{p}$. In crystals, symmetry requirements limit the number of units per turn along a screw axis to 2, 3, 4 and 6, but this limitation, which is set by the necessity to form a regular three-dimensional structure, need not apply to a molecule. The number of units per turn in a helical molecule, therefore, can have any value, and does not even have to be an integer. In projection on to the helix axis, the structure has a regular repeat period p. This gives rise to meridional reflections on the diffraction pattern.

The cross-like pattern which occurs at the centre of the continuous helix diffraction pattern will also occur in the pattern due to a discontinuous helix, and, in addition, will be repeated at each meridional reflection. This gives rise to characteristic diamond-shaped regions above and below the centre of the pattern (see plate IIIc).

If the discontinuous helix repeats itself in a distance c, then let the number of scattering points in this distance be M, and let the number of turns of the helix in this distance be N. Then $c = Mp = NP$. Because c is the repeat distance, the layer plane spacing in reciprocal space will be $\dfrac{1}{c}$, and the transform will only be finite at heights $Z = \dfrac{l}{c}$, where l is the layer plane number.

By considering a discontinuous helix as the points of intersection of a continuous helix and a set of equidistant planes of spacing p, the planes on which the transform is finite are given by

$$\frac{l}{c} = \frac{n}{p} + \frac{m}{p} \qquad \text{where } n \text{ and } m \text{ are integers.} \qquad (30)$$

The transform on the lth layer plane is

$$G\left(R, \psi, \frac{l}{c}\right) = \sum_n G\left(R, \psi, \frac{n}{p}\right) \qquad (31)$$

where the values of n in the summation must satisfy the previous equation.

In a helical molecule, the basic unit which repeats along the molecule consists of a number of different atoms. Each atom in the unit will have different co-ordinates and each will lie on a different helix. For the whole unit, therefore, there will be a set of helices of different radii, displaced relative to each other by rotation and translation. The transform of the molecule thus depends on the contribution of all these helices. When this is taken into account, the transform on the *l*th layer plane is given by

$$G\left(R, \psi, \frac{l}{c}\right) = \sum_n \sum_j f_j J_n(2\pi R r_j) \exp\left[i\left\{n\left(\psi - \phi_j + \frac{\pi}{2}\right) + \frac{2\pi l z_j}{c}\right\}\right]$$

(32)

where f_j is the scattering factor for the *j*th atom which has co-ordinates (r_j, ϕ_j, z_j).

Table 3 Some of the helical parameters of the α-helix, the *B* DNA double helix and tobacco mosaic virus particles.

Parameter	α-helix	B DNA	TMV
Pitch	5·4 Å	34 Å	23 Å
Number of residues per turn of the helix	3·6	10	$16\frac{1}{3}$
Vertical distance between residues	1·5 Å	3·4 Å	1·4 Å
Number of residues in the repeat distance	18	10	49

In contrast to the continuous helix transform, there is an *M*-fold variation in $\left|G\left(R, \psi, \frac{l}{c}\right)\right|$ as ψ varies from 0 to 360°.

Only the zero order Bessel function, $J_0(X)$, is finite when X is zero, hence the transform is finite when R is zero only when $n = 0$, i.e. when $Z = \frac{l}{c} = \pm\frac{1}{p}, \pm\frac{2}{p}$, etc., corresponding to $m = \pm 1, \pm 2$, etc. Therefore, there should be diffracted intensity along the meridian of the diffraction pattern (where $R = 0$) at positions corresponding to these values of Z.

In fibres which contain helical molecules, there is usually random rotational orientation about the helix axis, either of individual molecules, or of groups of molecules. If there is a continuous distribution of intensity along the layer lines in the diffraction pattern, it corresponds to the intensity due to a single molecule

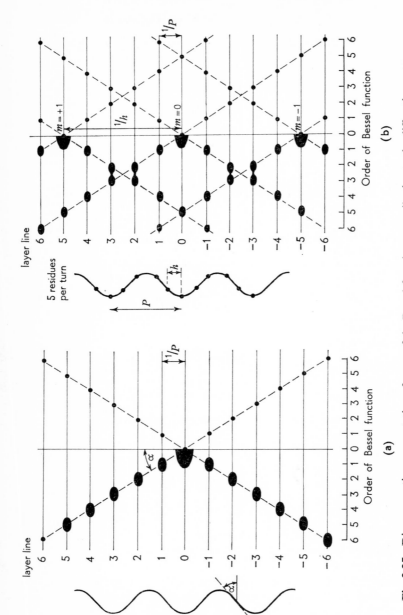

Fig. 2.25 Diagrammatic representation of some of the Bessel functions contributing to the diffraction pattern from (a) a continuous helix of pitch P, (b) a discontinuous helix with 5 units per turn, (c) a discontinuous helix with $5\frac{1}{3}$ units per turn, (d) a discontinuous helix with $2\frac{1}{8}$ units per turn. The dark regions on the left hand side of the diagrams correspond approximately to the first maxima of the Bessel functions.

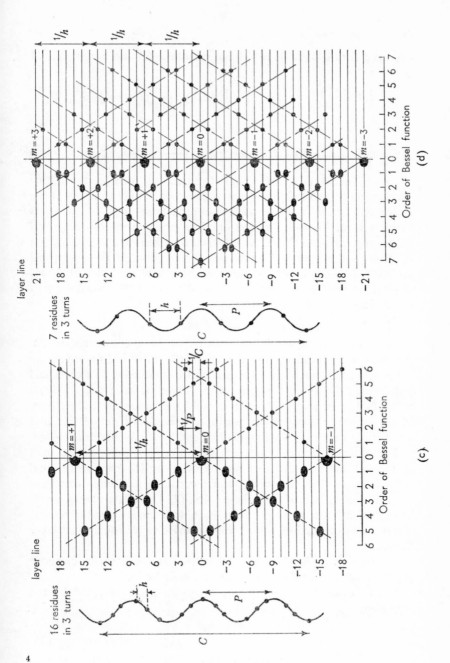

4

averaged for all possible rotational orientations; and is represented by

$$\left\langle I\left(R, \psi, \frac{l}{c}\right)\right\rangle_{\psi} = I\left(R, \frac{l}{c}\right) = \left\langle \left| G\left(R, \psi, \frac{l}{c}\right)\right|^{2}\right\rangle_{\psi} = \sum G_{n,l}^{2}(R)$$

(33)

$$\text{where } G_{n,l}(R) = \sum f_j J_n(2\pi Rr) \exp\left[i\left(\frac{2\pi z_j}{c} - n\phi_j\right)\right] \qquad (34)$$

When helical molecules pack together to form a crystalline arrangement, then the transform of the helix is only sampled at the reciprocal lattice points, and the observed intensity of the spots along a layer line will depend on their position in the reciprocal plane, and hence on the angle ψ. By rotating the calculated transform relative to the observed amplitude distribution in the reciprocal lattice, it is possible to find the position where the calculated and observed values agree, and hence to determine the orientation of the molecule in the unit cell.

c   The Fourier transform of a coiled-coil

The axis of a simple helix, such as we have considered in the previous section, follows a straight path. If the axis itself also follows a helical path, then the structure is called a coiled-coil. The helical path which the axis follows is called the major helix and the helix which is formed around this axis is called the minor helix. The theory of diffraction by a coiled-coil was first derived by Crick (1953), and was further developed by Lang (1956) and by Ramachandran (1960).

The main differences between the diffraction pattern due to a coiled-coil and that due to a simple helix are (1) extra meridional reflections occur on the coiled-coil pattern, at positions which are related to the pitch of the minor helix. (2) The effect of producing a coiled-coil from a simple helix is to split each layer line of the simple helix diffraction pattern into a series of closely spaced layer lines.

In order to explain these two results it is necessary to consider the form of the Fourier transform of a coiled-coil.

The co-ordinates of the major helix can be represented by the equations

$$\begin{aligned} x &= r_0 \cos\left(\omega_0 t + \phi_0\right) \\ y &= r_0 \sin\left(\omega_0 t + \phi_0\right) \\ z &= P(\omega_0 t/2\pi) \end{aligned}$$

(35)

where t is a parameter which is proportional to z; $\omega_0 = \dfrac{2\pi}{P} \cdot \dfrac{z}{t}$; P is the pitch of the helix; and ϕ_0 is the value of ϕ when $t = 0$.

The co-ordinates of the minor helix in a frame of reference which follows the major helix, (that is, with its origin on the major helix,

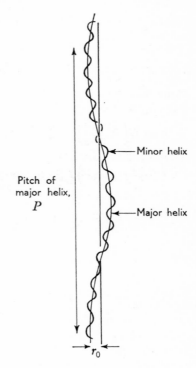

Fig. 2.26　Diagram of a coiled-coil.

Pitch of major helix, P

Minor helix

Major helix

r_0

a z' axis tangential to the major helix and an x' axis perpendicular to, and pointing away from the z axis) is given by

$$x' = r_1 \cos (\omega_1 t + \phi_1)$$
$$y' = r_1 \sin (\omega_1 t + \phi_1) \tag{36}$$
$$z' = 0.$$

If the major helix is assumed to be of different handedness to the minor helix, and makes N_0 turns while the minor helix makes N' turns (in its own frame of reference), in the same z-distance, c, then $-\omega_1/\omega_0 = N_1'/N_0$. The negative sign indicates the difference in handedness. Because of the difference in handedness, the number of turns of the minor helix, in an external frame of reference, is $N_1 = N_1' - N_0$.

Let the number of units in the repeat length, c, be M. Then the number of units per turn of the major helix is $n_0 = \dfrac{M}{N_0}$, the number of units per turn of the minor helix, in its own frame of reference is $n_1 = \dfrac{N}{N_1'}$, and the number per turn of the minor helix in an external frame of reference is $n = \dfrac{M}{N_1}$. Let t_0 be the value of t when the configuration repeats itself, then if there is an atom at $t = t_1$ we can write $\phi_M = 2\pi M t_1/t_0$. The Fourier transform of the M units is then given by $G\left(R, \psi, \dfrac{l}{c}\right) = \sum_p \sum_q \sum_s \sum_d J_p(2\pi R r_0) J_q(2\pi R \bar{r}_1)$

$$J_s\left(2\pi\left(\frac{l}{c}\right) r_1 \sin \alpha\right) J_d(2\pi R \Delta) \exp\left\{i\left[p\left(\psi - \phi_0 + \frac{\pi}{2}\right)\right.\right.$$

$$+ q\left(-\psi + \phi_1 + \frac{\pi}{2}\right) + s(\phi_1 + \pi)$$

$$\left.\left. + d\left(\psi + \phi_1 - \phi_0 + \frac{\pi}{2}\right) - m\phi_M + 2\pi z_0 \frac{l}{c}\right]\right\} \quad (37)$$

subject to the condition that

$$N_0 p + (N_1' - N_0)q + N_1' s + (N_1' + N_0) d - Mm = l \quad (38)$$

where p, q, s, d and m are integers.

The angle α determines the steepness of the major helix and is defined by $\tan \alpha = 2\pi r_0/P$ where r_0 and P are the radius and pitch, respectively, of the major helix.

The quantities $\bar{r}_1$ and Δ are defined by the equations

$$\bar{r}_1 = r_1(1 + \cos \alpha)/2 \quad (39)$$

$$\Delta = r_1(1 - \cos \alpha)/2 \quad (40)$$

For the coiled-coils that have been proposed as molecular structures, α is about $10°$ and it is possible to write $\bar{r}_1 \doteqdot r_1$ and $\Delta \doteqdot 0$. These approximations simplify the interpretation of the Fourier transform expression.

The coiled-coil transform is more complicated than that for a simple coil, but, because $J_n(x)$ is small when x is small and n is large many of the Bessel function terms can be neglected. The solution also depends on the product of four Bessel function terms so that if one of them is small the product will also be small. Because $\Delta \doteq 0$, then if $J_d(2\pi R\Delta)$ is to be finite d must be zero.

We are now in a position to see how the extra meridional reflections and the splitting of layer lines arise in the case of diffraction by a coiled-coil.

(i) If $p = q = s = 0$ and $m = 1$, then $l = M$ and a meridional intensity is observed. This is due to the regular repeat distance between the units. If this vertical distance is h, then the intensity occurs at the reciprocal spacing $\dfrac{1}{h}$. A similar meridional intensity occurs at $\dfrac{1}{h'}$, where $h = h' \cos \alpha$, if there is no coiled-coiling, and in this case, would be the first meridional intensity.

In the case of the coiled-coil, however, it is also possible to obtain a meridional intensity if $p = q = 0$ and $s \neq 0$, because the term $J_s(2\pi r_1 \sin \alpha)$ does not include R and can be finite when $R = 0$, on the meridian. A meridional intensity can thus be observed when $p = q = m = 0$ and $s = 1$, when $l = N_1'$. This intensity on the meridian is closer to the centre of the pattern than the one due to the repeat distance between units, and corresponds to a spacing equal to the pitch of the minor helix.

(ii)   If $s = 0$, then $N_0 p + (N_1' - N_0)q + Mm = l.$ (41)

This equation may be compared with the related one for a simple helix,

$$Nq + Mm = l$$

where N corresponds to $(N_1' - N_0)$.

Now $N_0 p \ll (N_1' - N_0)q$, so that the effect of making a coiled-coil out of a simple helix is to split up each layer line of the simple helix pattern into a series of closely spaced layer lines when p has the values $0, \pm 1, \pm 2$, etc.

While the 'allowed' positions of the intensity on the diffraction pattern are determined by the periodicities of the coiled-coil, the actual intensity distribution within these regions is governed by the

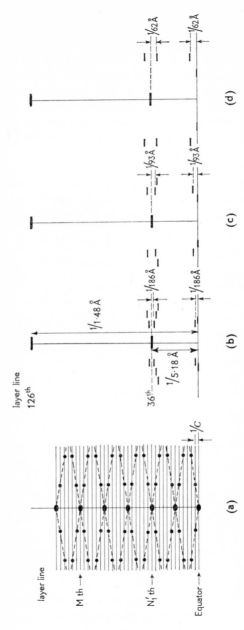

Fig. 2.27 (a) Diagrammatic representation of some of the possible features of the diffraction pattern due to a single-stranded coiled-coil with M residues in the repeat period, c, in which the major helix makes one turn and the minor helix N'_1 turns (in its own frame of reference), and where there is an integral number of residues in two turns of the minor helix.

(b) Some of the expected features in the diffraction pattern due to a single stranded α-helix coiled-coil.

(c) Due to a double stranded α-helix coiled-coil of parallel chains.

(d) Due to a triple stranded α-helix coiled-coil of parallel chains.

atomic positions in the structure. For n atoms (with scattering factors f) in the repeating unit, the Fourier transform is given by

$$G\left(R, \psi, \frac{l}{c}\right) = \sum_{j=1}^{n} f_j G_j\left(R, \psi, \frac{l}{c}\right) \qquad (42)$$

An alternative way of looking at diffraction from a coiled-coil is to consider the major helix as a simple helix, but with a repeating unit which consists of a group of residues (Fraser, MacRae and Miller, 1964). Thus the α-helix coiled-coil, for example, can be considered as a simple helix with a pitch equal to that of the major helix, but with a repeating unit consisting of seven residues—the number which occurs in two turns of the minor helix in its own frame of reference.

Table 4 Parameters of the coiled-coil chain conformations proposed for α-keratin and collagen

Parameter	α-Keratin	Collagen
Major helix radius, r_0	5·3 Å	2·6 Å
Major helix pitch, P	186 Å	85·6 Å
Vertical distance (parallel to z-axis) between residues	1·48 Å	2·86 Å
Number of turns of major helix in repeat distance, N_0	1	1
Number of residues in the repeat distance	126	30
Number of turns of minor helix (in its own frame of reference) in repeat distance, N_1'	36	10
Number of residues per turn of the minor helix (in its own frame of reference), n_1	3·5	3

14 Low Angle X-ray Scattering

The region of the diffraction pattern near the direct beam is referred to as the low angle region. There is an inverse relationship between the diffraction angle and the spacing in the diffracting object, so that the low angle diffraction gives information about the large scale structure of molecules rather than about their atomic structure. Thus, low angle scattering can give information about the general shape of large molecules, and the scattering is dependent on the difference between the average electron density within the molecule and that of the surrounding medium.

If we consider a dilute solution of identical particles placed in an x-ray beam, then the scattered intensity is proportional to the intensity scattered by a single particle, averaged for all possible orientations. For spherically symmetrical particles the Fourier transform of the electron density, $\rho(r)$, is given by

$$G(R) = \int_0^\infty \rho(r) \frac{\sin(2\pi Rr)}{2\pi Rr} 4\pi r^2 \, dr \tag{43}$$

or, by inverse transformation

$$\rho(r) = \int_0^\infty G(R) \frac{\sin(2\pi Rr)}{2\pi Rr} 2R^2 \, dR \tag{44}$$

Hence, if $G(R)$ is determined experimentally, $\rho(r)$, can be calculated.

If we consider the case of cylindrically symmetrical particles with their axes parallel to each other and perpendicular to the x-ray beam, then the Fourier transform at a distance R along the zero layer plane is given by

$$G(R) = \int_0^\infty 2\pi r \rho(r) J_0(2\pi Rr) \, dr \tag{45}$$

where $J_0(2\pi Rr)$ is a zero order Bessel function.

The radial distribution of electron density is then given by

$$\rho(r) = \int_0^\infty 2\pi R G(R) J_0(2\pi Rr) \, dR. \tag{46}$$

15   Experimental Methods

a   Production of x-rays

X-rays are produced when a beam of high energy electrons strike a target. The electrons are produced by electrically heating a tungsten filament, and they are accelerated by a potential difference, of the order of tens of kilovolts, between the filament and the target. Both filament and target are situated in an evacuated tube. X-rays

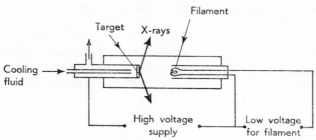

Fig. 2.28   Production of x-rays.

which are produced at the target pass out of the tube through a window made of low absorbing material.

b   X-ray wavelengths

The distribution of intensity from a target consists of sharp peaks superimposed on a continuous background of intensity. The sharp peaks are the characteristic spectrum of the target material, and its production can be explained in terms of the energy levels of the atoms of the target. The continuous radiation is referred to as

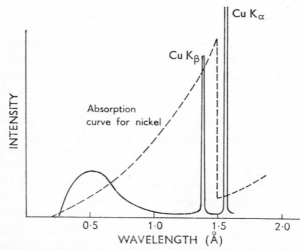

Fig. 2.29   Distribution of wavelength from an x-ray tube (full line), and the absorption curve for a filter (dashed line) which has an absorption edge between the K_α and K_β lines, and which absorbs most of the K_β radiation.

'white' radiation and is due to the retardation of the electrons within the target.

For x-ray structure analysis it is usual to use monochromatic radiation, so that one peak is selected from the characteristic spectrum. Selection of one emission line can be made by absorption of unwanted radiation by a filter, or by means of a crystal monochromator.

c   Detection of x-rays

The most common method of recording diffraction patterns is by means of a photographic film. By measuring the amount of blackening of the film the relative intensities of different parts of the diffraction pattern can be determined.

In recent years there has been an increase in the use of ionization and scintillation counter methods of measuring diffracted intensities, because these methods give a higher degree of accuracy and also can be made automatic.

d   X-ray cameras

The x-rays emitted from an x-ray tube are usually collimated by means of pin holes in order to produce an approximately parallel, narrow beam. The usual procedure with fibrous and non-crystalline specimens is to keep them stationary in the x-ray beam and to record the diffraction pattern either on a flat or a cylindrical film. The collimating system and film holder constitute the x-ray camera. When the exposure times are very long it is necessary to evacuate the camera, or to keep it filled with hydrogen, in order to eliminate air scattering.

Single crystal specimens are either mounted at the end of a thin glass fibre or in a thin-walled glass tube, which, in turn, is mounted on a goniometer head by means of which the crystal can be set at any angle relative to the x-ray beam. The crystal is usually set so that it can be rotated or oscillated about an axis parallel to one of the unit cell axes. Because of overlap of spectra in rotation and oscillation photographs, special cameras are used in order to record the diffracted spectra in a systematic manner. The most common of these cameras are the Weissenberg and the precession cameras, in which the film is moved in phase with the crystal oscillation, and screens are arranged to cut off unwanted spectra. Each diffraction photograph taken with these cameras gives information about a section of reciprocal space. By taking a series of photographs, the three-dimensional distribution of intensity within the limiting sphere can be obtained.

The problem of measuring the intensities of a large number of spots on a photographic film is a formidable one, and during the past few years automatic counter diffractometers have been developed to overcome this.

e Determination of structure amplitudes

The measured intensity of diffracted spectra depends on the experimental arrangement as well as on the atomic structure of the specimen. The measured diffracted intensity from a rotating single crystal is related to the structure factors by the equation

$$I(hkl) = K|F(hkl)|^2 \, Lp \qquad (47)$$

where K is a constant, but L and p depend on the angle of diffraction. The factor L is known as the Lorentz factor and depends on the time the particular set of planes remain in a reflecting position. The polarization factor, p, takes into account the state of polarization of the diffracted x-ray beam. Both L and p can be calculated for the various experimental arrangements used for measuring intensities.

If the constant K in equation (47) is ignored, only the relative values of the structure amplitudes will be determined. In order to obtain the correct electron densities in Fourier syntheses, however, it is necessary to place the structure amplitudes on an absolute scale, so that K has to be determined. There are three ways in which this can be done:

(a) By comparison of the diffracted intensities with the intensity of the incident x-ray beam.

(b) By comparison of the intensities with those of known absolute intensity from a standard crystal.

(c) By a graphical method based on a theory developed by Wilson (1942).

16 Methods of Structure Determination

The fact that only the amplitude of diffracted rays can be directly determined from the measured diffracted intensities has already been mentioned. In order to make a direct structure determination, however, the phases of the diffracted rays must also be known. This lack of information about the phases, known as the 'phase problem', is the obstacle which methods of structure determination must overcome. Whatever method is used, the usual test for the correctness of a proposed structure is the agreement between the observed diffracted amplitudes and those calculated from the proposed structure. In the case of crystalline specimens the degree of agreement is expressed by a factor R where

$$R = \frac{\sum ||F_0| - |F_c||}{\sum |F_0|} \tag{48}$$

and $|F_0|$ and $|F_c|$ are the observed and calculated amplitudes respectively.

The lower the R factor the better is the agreement between observed and calculated amplitudes. Structure determination proceeds in stages, and at each successive stage a more accurate picture of the structure is obtained. This process is indicated by a reduction in the R factor, which, in the final stages of the structure determination of small organic molecules is usually less than 0·10.

a   Trial and error

In the trial and error method of structure determination a plausible structure is proposed, based on the intensity of some of the outstandingly strong diffracted spectra, on the packing limitations imposed by the symmetry, and on chemical knowledge. If the diffracted intensity from a particular set of planes is large it can be assumed that a large proportion of the atoms in the structure lie close to these planes. By considering a few of the strong spectra it may then be possible to determine reasonable positions for the atoms. Using these positions in a trial structure, the diffracted amplitudes are calculated and compared with the experimental values. The atomic positions are then modified in a systematic manner until the agreement between the observed and calculated amplitudes is as good as the experimental accuracy will allow.

Trial and error methods have been successful in solving many crystal structures and it is also the method that has been used in the analysis of fibrous protein and nucleic acid structures.

b   The Patterson synthesis

Because of the lack of information about the phases of the diffracted spectra, Patterson (1934) investigated the effect of using the squares of the amplitudes, which are directly determined from the measured intensities. Patterson defined a function $P(uvw)$ where

$$P_{(uvw)} = V \int_0^1 \int_0^1 \int_0^1 \rho(xyz)\rho(x + u, y + u, z + w)\, dx\, dy\, dz \quad (49)$$

where V is the volume of the unit cell and $\rho(xyz)$ and $\rho(x + u, y + u, z + w)$ are the electron densities at the points with fractional co-ordinates (xyz) and $(x + u, y + v, z + w)$ respectively.

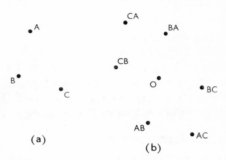

Fig. 2.30 (a) An arrangement of atoms. (b) The Patterson map for the arrangement in (a).

If we substitute for $\rho(xyz)$ and $\rho(x + u, y + u, z + w)$ in equation (49), and use the relation $|F(\overline{hkl})| = |F(hkl)|$, we obtain

$$P(uvw) = \frac{1}{V} \sum_h \sum_k \sum_{l=-\infty}^{\infty} |F(hkl)|^2 \cos(hx + ky + lz). \quad (50)$$

This series can be summed without any knowledge of the phases, because it only involves the squares of the structure amplitudes. Equation (49) shows that the function $P(uvw)$ has large values only when both $\rho(xyz)$ and $\rho(x + u, y + v, z + w)$ have large values. Thus $P(uvw)$ is large when two regions of electron density are separated by a vector with components (uvw). The electron density in a structure has peaks at the atomic positions, so that a peak in the function $P(uvw)$ represents interatomic vectors. Thus, if there are n atoms in a structure there will be n^2 peaks in the Patterson function, n of which are superimposed at the origin and $n(n - 1)$ are non-origin peaks.

To illustrate how a Patterson function is related to the atomic distribution we consider a structure composed of three atoms (Fig. 2.30). The theoretical Patterson is obtained by placing each atom in turn at an origin and marking the positions of the other atoms. This gives rise to six non-origin peaks and shows that the Patterson map is centrosymmetric although the structure itself is non-centrosymmetric.

The value of $P(uvw)$ at the end of a vector between two atoms of atomic numbers Z_n and Z_m is equal to Z_nZ_m. This means that if there is an atom of high atomic number in a structure then the vectors between these atoms should show up clearly in a Patterson map. In order to obtain the correct magnitude of peaks in a Patterson synthesis the absolute values of the structure factors should be known, and $|F_{000}|^2$ should be included in the summation in equation (50).

The larger the number of atoms there are in a structure, the more difficult it becomes to interpret the Patterson synthesis because of the large amount of overlap of peaks, since the n^2 peaks occupy the same volume as the n atoms of the structure. Details of the methods of analysis of Patterson maps are given by Buerger (1959).

c The heavy atom method

If a molecule contains an atom with a high atomic number then the scattering from this atom will be much greater than from the other atoms in the molecule and will dominate the amplitude and phase of the various spectra.

The position of the heavy atom can be determined from a Patterson synthesis and its contribution to the phases of the various spectra can then be calculated. A Fourier synthesis is then carried out using the measured diffracted amplitudes and the phases of the heavy atom alone. These phases will not be exactly correct but they should be approximate enough to reveal some of the lighter atoms in the Fourier maps. These lighter atoms, together with the heavy atom, are now used to calculate new phases which should be closer to the correct values than those calculated for the heavy atom alone. A second Fourier is then calculated using the new phases, when more of the light atoms should be revealed in the maps. These new atoms are included in another phase calculation and the process is repeated until all the atoms in the structure are revealed in the Fourier maps.

The atomic number of a heavy atom should be large enough to make a significant contribution to the resultant phases, but should not be too large, otherwise the lighter atoms can not be located. A rough rule for determining the suitability of a heavy atom is that the square of its atomic number should be approximately equal to the sum of the squares of the atomic numbers of the light atoms.

The most complex structure that has been solved by the heavy atom technique is that of vitamin B_{12} by Hodgkin and her collaborators (Hodgkin *et al.*, 1957). Vitamin B_{12} contains nearly a hundred atoms (excluding hydrogen) one of which is a cobalt atom of atomic number 27 and which functions as a heavy atom.

d Isomorphous replacement

The method of isomorphous replacement is the one that has been successful in the analysis of crystalline protein structures. In this method a comparison is made between the diffraction patterns of related structures which differ only slightly from each other and which have the same unit cell dimensions. Thus the method was used by Robertson (1936) in the analysis of phthalocyanine which is isomorphous with its nickel derivative. For protein structure analysis a comparison is made between the diffraction pattern of a protein crystal and that of a crystal of protein plus a heavy atom.

The structure factors of the heavy atom derivative, represented by F_H, is the vector sum of the contributions due to the protein, F, and that due to the heavy atom, f. Thus,

$$F_H = F + f \tag{51}$$

The first step in the analysis is to locate the heavy atom. This is done by means of a Patterson synthesis using $(|F_H| - |F|)^2$ as coefficients. Although protein molecules crystallize in non-centrosymmetric space groups, certain projections are usually centrosymmetric. For example, in the space group $P2_1$ the projection down the two-fold screw axis is centrosymmetric. It is much easier to determine the co-ordinates in these projections because the phases are either 0 or 180°, so that the structure factors are either $+ |F|$ or $- |F|$.

In order to determine the phases by the isomorphous method, at least two heavy atom derivatives are normally required. The third co-ordinates of the heavy atoms are determined by means of a Patterson synthesis using $(|F_{H_1}| - |F_{H_2}|)^2$ as coefficients (Rossman, 1960). The resulting Patterson maps show positive peaks due to H_1H_1 and H_2H_2 vectors, and negative peaks representing H_1H_2 vectors.

After the heavy atoms have been located, various parameters, such as their position and effective atomic number, are refined. The effective atomic number is less than the true atomic number because the heavy atom may not attach itself to every molecule in the crystal. After refinement, the amplitude and phase of the heavy atom contribution to the various spectra can be calculated. The phases of the spectra can then be determined graphically from a phase-amplitude diagram (Harker, 1956).

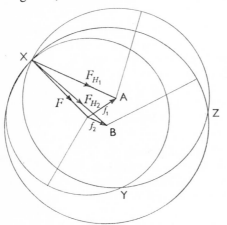

Fig. 2.31 Phase determination with two isomorphous derivatives. F represents the structure factor of the native protein; F_{H_1} and F_{H_2} those of the heavy atom derivatives, and f_1 and f_2 those of the heavy atoms themselves.

The amplitude and phase of the heavy atom contribution are represented by the magnitude and direction of the line OA (Fig. 2.31). This line forms one side of a vector triangle, the other two sides being the structure factor of the native protein, F, and the structure factor of the heavy atom derivative, F_H. However, only the amplitudes of these structure factors are known. Hence, with centre 0, a circle of radius $|F|$ is drawn, and with centre A, a circle of radius $|F_H|$. The two circles intersect at two points, X and Y, which thus form the possible third corner of the triangle. In order to distinguish between the alternatives, X and Y, a second heavy atom derivative is required, with the heavy atom occupying a different site. The amplitude and phase of the second heavy atom contribution is represented by OB and the intersections of the two circles now occur at X and Z. The direction of XO thus gives the phase of the protein structure factor.

In practice, the phase determination is not always as clear cut as Fig. 2.31 suggests, and it is desirable to use more than two heavy atom derivatives. From the results of a number of derivatives the best value of the phase for a particular structure factor can be determined, and a 'figure of merit' given to represent the reliability of the phase determination (Blow and Crick, 1959). The Fourier synthesis calculated using the best phases, and with amplitudes weighted by the figure of merit, is the one that is most error free.

An alternative method of phase determination, which requires only one heavy atom derivative, can be applied if use is made of anomalous scattering. Under normal diffraction conditions $|F(hkl)|$ $= |F(\overline{hkl})|$ even if the structure is non-centrosymmetric. This condition is known as Friedel's law. It means that it is then impossible to distinguish between two enantiomorphous structures. Also under normal conditions the phase change suffered by the scattered x-rays is constant, and is the same for all the atoms in the structure. However, if the wavelength of the incident radiation is close to an absorption edge of an atom in the structure, then the scattered wave suffers an anomalous phase shift which is slightly in advance of the normal phase. This gives rise to a difference in intensity between (hkl) and $(\overline{hkl})$ spectra.

Anomalous scattering effects were first demonstrated with zinc sulphide crystals and gold radiation, by Koster, Knol and Prins (1930), and were used by Bijvoet and his co-workers (Peerdeman, Bommel and Bijvoet, 1951) in the first determination of the absolute configuration of a molecule.

Anomalous scattering from a single heavy atom derivative can resolve the ambiguity in the phase, which, in the general case requires a second derivative to resolve (Ramachandran and Raman, 1956). Blow and Rossmann (1961) have applied the method to haemoglobin and haemoglobin $+ 4HgCl_2$.

e Direct phase determination

Crystal structures have certain properties which makes it possible to relate the phases of structure factors. These properties are very general ones, such as the fact that the electron density is never negative, or that atoms are approximately spherical in shape. When these conditions are expressed in a mathematical form it is possible to derive relationships between the phases of the structure factors. These methods are outside the scope of this monograph, and the standard textbooks should be consulted for further details.

One direct method of phase determination which may be applicable to protein and virus structures has been proposed by Rossmann and Blow (1961, 1963). It is applicable when a molecule is built up from a number of identical subunits, or when there are more than one molecule in an asymmetric unit. In such cases there is additional, non-crystallographic symmetry. From an analysis of the Patterson synthesis it is possible to determine the amount of rotation and translation that is required to make one molecule (or subunit) parallel to, and bring it into coincidence with another. It is then possible to relate the phases of different structure factors, using the criterion that the electron density in the molecules (or subunits) is the same.

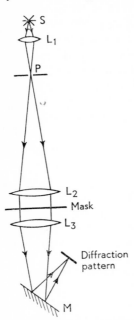

Fig. 2.32 Schematic diagram of the Lipson-Taylor optical diffractometer.

17   Optical Transforms

The calculations of structure factors and Fourier syntheses which are involved in structure analysis are very lengthy, and for large molecules would be virtually impossible without the use of high speed computers.

In the analysis of fibre diagrams, a method which has been particularly useful is that of optical diffraction, as developed in the optical diffractometer by Lipson, Taylor and their co-workers. The recent text book by Taylor and Lipson (1964) gives full details of the optical diffraction method. In addition to being particularly elegant, the method emphasises the physical principles involved in x-ray diffraction.

The arrangement of the optical diffractometer is illustrated in Fig. 2.32. S is a source of light which is focused on to a pin-hole P which acts as a secondary source. The lenses L_2 and L_3 have a focal length of about 1·5 metres and a mirror M is so arranged that the focal plane of L_3 can be viewed with a microscope. If an object is placed between the lenses L_2 and L_3, its Fraunhofer diffraction pattern is observed in the focal plane of L_3.

If a mask is prepared by punching holes to represent atoms, then a projection of a proposed structure can be prepared, and its Fraunhofer diffraction pattern compared with the x-ray diffraction pattern. In a fibre diagram, the resultant pattern is that due to molecules in all possible orientations about the fibre axis, so that a number of masks have to be prepared corresponding to different projections of the structure. Stokes (1955,a) has shown that if the optical diffraction pattern is to simulate the fibre pattern down to a spacing of d_0, then the angles between the projections should be slightly less than d_0/D radian, where D is the diameter of the molecule. Thus the total number of projections should be about $2\pi D/d_0$. In the case of a helical molecule the number will be reduced because the projections are unchanged when the molecule is turned through an angle of $2\pi/m$ radian where m is the number of units per turn of the helix. For a helical molecule, therefore, the number of projections should be about $2\pi D/md_0$.

3 Proteins

1 Introduction

Proteins form one of the main groups of molecules found in living matter. They perform many different functions and vary widely in their chemical activity. Some proteins, such as keratin of wool and hair, or collagen of tendon, are relatively inert, while the enzymes, which are also protein molecules, are highly reactive and catalyze chemical reactions in the cell.

Protein molecules are polymers of amino acids which are linked together to form a polypeptide chain. There are twenty commonly occurring amino acids in proteins, together with a few other rarer amino acids which are closely related to the commonly occurring ones.

Amino acids in neutral solution can be represented by the formula $H_3\overset{+}{N}$. CH(R) . COO$^-$, where R represents the group that differs from one amino acid to another. The chemical properties of these groups vary considerably. Some of them are non-polar whereas others are polar and can partake in hydrogen bond formation. Glutamic and aspartic acid contain acidic groups while arginine and lysine contain basic groups. Cysteine and methionine contain sulphur atoms but whereas the sulphur atom in cysteine is highly reactive, the one in methionine is not.

Proline is unusual because a carbon atom of the R group is bonded to the imino nitrogen atom. This means that proline can not form hydrogen bonds in the same way as other amino acids when it is in a polypeptide chain.

To form a polypeptide chain, the amino acids link together by the elimination of water so that the chain can be represented as

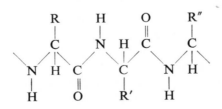

The carbon atom of the CH group in the chain is called the C_α atom; the first carbon atom of the R group is C_β, the second is C_γ, and so on.

All the amino acids except glycine are optically active and of the two possible configurations only the *L* form is found in proteins. Looking down on to the tetrahedron along the HC direction, the

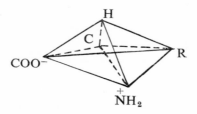

R group, amino group and carboxyl group follow each other in a clockwise direction in this configuration. This absolute configuration is known from x-ray diffraction studies which take into account the anomalous scattering of x-rays (Trommel and Bijvoet, 1954).

Proteins may be divided into two classes: fibrous and globular. Fibrous proteins usually contain long polypeptide chains lying parallel or nearly parallel to each other. In globular proteins the polypeptide chains are folded to form compact molecules.

Many globular proteins can be extracted from cells, purified, and crystallized. Their structure can then be investigated by single crystal x-ray analysis in a similar way to that of smaller organic molecules. The only difference is the greater complexity of the problem due to the larger number of atoms in a protein molecule. The first x-ray diffraction photographs from a crystalline globular protein were obtained from pepsin crystals by Bernal and Crowfoot in 1934. Shortly afterwards diffraction photographs were obtained from insulin crystals (Crowfoot, 1935) and from haemoglobin crystals (Bernal, Fankuchen and Perutz, 1938). These photographs showed a large number of reflections, which meant that if the phases could be determined, a direct determination of the molecular structure would be possible. Phase determination, however, remained an obstacle until Perutz (Green, Ingram and Perutz, 1954) discovered that the isomorphous replacement method could be applied to protein crystal analysis.

The structure determination of fibrous proteins had to be approached in a different manner. X-ray diffraction photographs

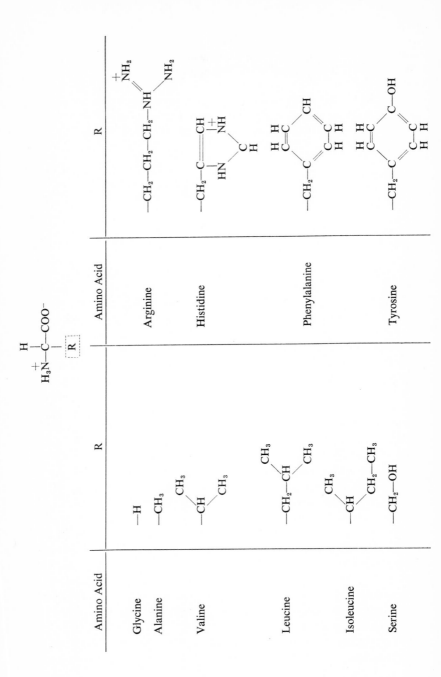

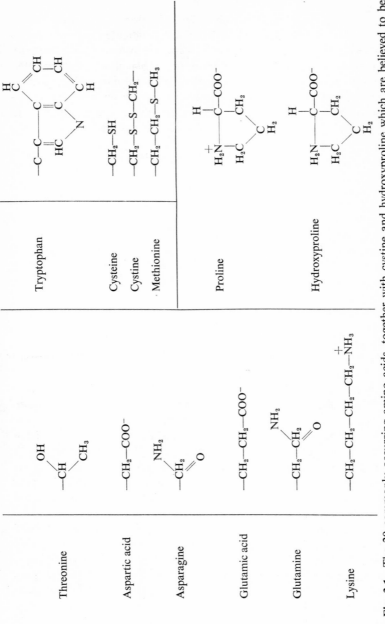

Fig. 3.1 The 20 commonly occurring amino acids, together with cystine and hydroxyproline which are believed to be formed from cysteine and proline respectively after these have been incorporated into a polypeptide chain.

from fibrous proteins show only a few reflections, and some of these are often rather diffuse. These reflections indicate the main periodicities in the structure but are too few to make possible a direct structure determination. This meant that plausible structures had to be postulated, and, because of the small amount of information on the x-ray diffraction patterns, this left plenty of room for speculation. It was necessary, therefore, to define general but rigid steriochemical rules by means of which unsatisfactory structures could be eliminated.

Although we are primarily concerned with the x-ray diffraction studies, it should be borne in mind that other techniques have been useful and are very important in the study of fibrous proteins. In particular, the results of polarized infra-red radiation studies were important in determining the orientations of the N—H and C—O bonds relative to the fibre axis.

The first x-ray studies of fibrous proteins were made by Herzog and Janke (1920), who obtained diffraction photographs from muscle, hair, nerve and silk. This was followed by a detailed study of silk by Brill (1923) who indexed the reflections in terms of a unit cell with a period of 7·0 Å along the fibre axis, and Meyer and Mark (1928) suggested that this periodicity was due to fully extended polypeptide chains lying parallel to each other.

Astbury and his co-workers (Astbury and Street, 1931; Astbury and Woods, 1933; Astbury, 1938) made a systematic x-ray study of many fibrous proteins and discovered that it was possible to classify them by means of their x-ray diffraction patterns into two main groups, the keratin-myosin-epidermin-fibrinogen (*k-m-e-f*) group, and the collagen group. Some members of the *k-m-e-f* group existed in what was called the α-conformation, while others existed in a β-conformation. Wool keratin in the natural state was in the α-conformation but, after extension under suitable conditions of humidity and temperature, it changed into the more extended β-conformation.

Astbury and Woods (1933) proposed that in β-keratin, extended polypeptide chains were bonded together to form sheets, and this forms the basis of the presently accepted model for β-structures. The folded conformation proposed by Astbury for α-proteins, however, proved eventually to be less satisfactory (Astbury and Bell, 1941; Astbury, 1941).

In an attempt to eliminate unsatisfactory models of polypeptide chain conformations, Huggins (1943) formulated a set of steriochemical requirements which had to be satisfied by any proposed structure. This was followed by a systematic survey of possible polypeptide chain conformations by Bragg, Kendrew and Perutz (1950), who accepted some and rejected others of Huggins's requirements. However, definite conclusions about the relative merits of a number of models could not be made.

A major advance in the elucidation of protein structure occurred in 1951, when Pauling and Corey proposed new models for the structure of synthetic α-polypeptides, the α and β forms of the *k-m-e-f* group, collagen, feather keratin and haemoglobin. The most important model to emerge from this work was the α-helix, which was proposed as the polypeptide chain conformation in the α-type structures. In constructing these new models, Pauling and Corey applied more rigid steriochemical rules than those of Huggins and of Bragg, Kendrew and Perutz. The rules applied were given by Pauling, Corey and Bronson (1951), and are as follows:

(*a*) All the residues are equivalent (except for the differences in the R groups beyond C_β). The general way of producing equivalent residues is to have helical conformations.

(*b*) Each amide group should be planar. This was supported by the structure analysis of amides. The structure analysis also showed a shortening of the C—N bond from the normal single bond length of 1·47 to 1·32 Å and a lengthening of the C—O bond from the double bond value of 1·215 to 1·24 Å. This suggested resonance between the two structures

so that the atoms of the amide group would be expected to be coplanar.

(*c*) Interatomic distances and angles should be the same as those obtained from single crystal studies of related simple substances.

(*d*) Each nitrogen atom forms a hydrogen bond with an oxygen atom of another residue. The nitrogen-oxygen distance was taken as 2·72 Å, and the maximum allowed deviation of the N—H bond from the N—O direction was 30°.

In addition to these requirements, no restriction was imposed on the number of residues per turn of the helix, so that the concept of a non-integral helix was introduced for the first time.

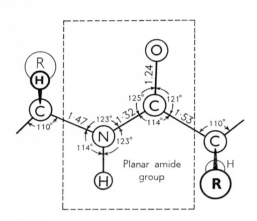

Fig. 3.2 Bond lengths and angles in polypeptide chains as derived from single crystal x-ray analysis of amino acids and peptides. (From Corey and Pauling, 1955.)

The most satisfactory model which incorporated these requirements was the α-helix. It had a pitch of 5·4 Å and contained 3·6 residues per turn. Each residue was hydrogen bonded to the fourth residue further along the chain so that the hydrogen bonds were parallel to the helix axis. The vertical distance between residues was 1·5 Å, and this should give rise to a meridional reflection on the x-ray pattern. In order to observe such a reflection, it is necessary to tilt the specimen relative to the x-ray beam, and by doing this with a synthetic α-polypeptide fibre and with hair, Perutz (1951) demonstrated the presence of this reflection. It had been recorded earlier on photographs from porcupine quill by MacArthur (1943), and it was also obtained from muscle fibres (Huxley and Perutz, 1951). The presence of the 1·5 Å reflection was thus strong evidence in favour of the α-helix as the basic polypeptide conformation in these structures.

Shortly after Pauling and Corey's proposals, Cochran, Crick and Vand (1952) developed the theory of diffraction by a helical structure and applied it to analyse the diffraction pattern of poly-γ-methyl-L-glutamate (Cochran and Crick, 1952). This analysis showed that the pattern was due to a helical structure with the parameters of the α-helix. Thus, the model building of Pauling and Corey, and the helical diffraction theory, suggested the same structure.

Although the α-helix was in agreement with the x-ray diffraction patterns from synthetic polypeptides, it had to be modified in order to account for the α-keratin pattern. In this modification, proposed independently by Crick (1952) and by Pauling and Corey (1953b), the α-helices are twisted round each other to form a coiled-coil.

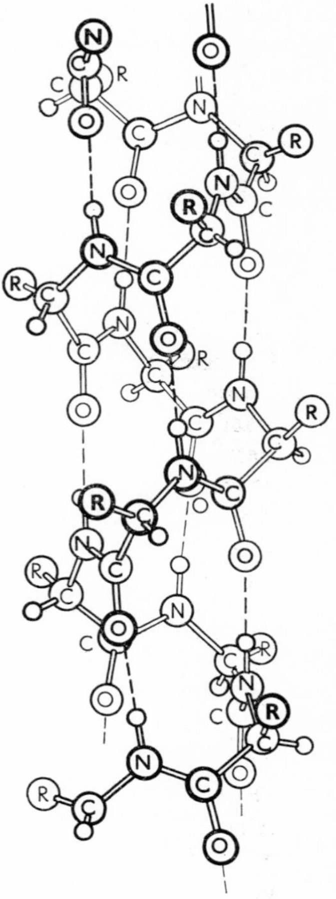

An acceptable model for the structure of the other main group of fibrous proteins, the collagen group, was not forthcoming until more recently, although numerous unacceptable models had been previously proposed.

In 1953, Cohen and Bear, and Cowan, North and Randall showed that the diffraction patterns suggested a helical structure. Ramachandran and Kartha (1954) proposed that in collagen, three parallel, helical chains were hydrogen bonded together to form a unit. This model was later modified so that the three helical chains formed a coiled-coil arrangement (Ramachandran and Kartha, 1955).

Fig. 3.3 A right-handed α-helix. (From Corey and Pauling, 1955.)

A similar conformation for the polypeptide chains in collagen was also derived by Rich and Crick (1955), by Cowan, McGavin and North (1955) and by Bear (1956).

2   Amino Acids and Peptides

The importance of single crystal structure analysis of amino acids and peptides in establishing the steriochemical principles that apply in protein structure has already been referred to. Experimental confirmation of Pauling and Corey's proposal of the planarity of the amide group came from the x-ray analysis of N-acetyl-glycine (Carpenter and Donohue, 1950), β-glycylglycine (Hughes and Moore, 1949) and diketopiperazine (Corey, 1938). Since 1951 the structures of many other amino acids and peptides have been determined and have confirmed the Pauling and Corey postulates.

3   α-Structures

a   *Synthetic polypeptides*

Synthetic polypeptides have structures which are closely related to those of fibrous proteins, and they often give more detailed diffraction patterns. The first synthetic α-polypeptide to be studied in detail was poly-γ-methyl-L-glutamate (PMG). X-ray diffraction photographs were obtained from oriented films of PMG by Bamford, Hanby and Happey (1951); and Pauling and Corey (1951b) proposed that the polypeptide chain was in the α-helical conformation. The α-helix parameters were in agreement with the diffraction pattern when it was analysed in terms of the helical diffraction theory by Cochran Crick, and Vand (1952). A more detailed analysis by Bamford *et al.* (1953) showed that a slightly modified α-helix with 3·625 residues per turn was preferable to the 3·6 residue helix. Similar analysis of poly-L-alanine (PLA) suggested a helix with 3·615 residues per turn (Bamford *et al.*, 1954).

The parameters of the helix are determined from the layer line spacing and the meridional reflections, but the distribution of intensity along the layer lines depend on the atomic positions in the structure. The intensity distribution along the layer lines of the PLA diffraction pattern was shown to be in agreement with a random up and down arrangement of right-handed α-helices containing L-type residues (Elliott and Malcolm, 1956 and 1959).

Several other synthetic polypeptides give characteristic α-type diffraction patterns, indicating the presence of polypeptide chains in the α-helical conformation, although the number of residues per turn of the helix may vary slightly from one polymer to another.

Poly-β-benzyl-L-aspartate (PBA) shows interesting properties in solution, and optical rotation measurements suggest that the helix is left-handed. Under certain conditions, PBA gives a poor α-type diffraction pattern, but if it is heated to 160° and then cooled, it gives a much sharper pattern which can be interpreted in terms of

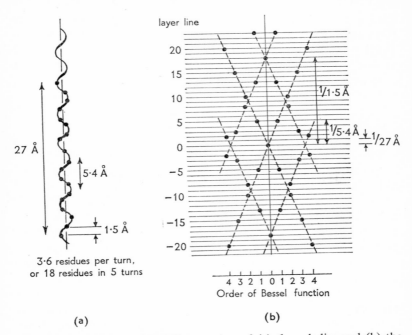

Fig. 3.4   A diagrammatic representation of (a) the α-helix, and (b) the Bessel functions contributing to the x-ray diffraction pattern.

a structure similar to the α-helix, but with four residues per turn. This was a conformation which had been considered by Bragg *et al.* (1950) in their survey of possible polypeptide chain conformations.

It is fair to summarize by saying that the basic conformation of the polypeptide chains in these polypeptides is the α-helix, but that in some cases, when the molecules pack together in a fibre, interactions may take place so as to produce a conformation of lower energy, as in PBA. The most common form of the α-helix is the right-handed form, but the left-handed form also occurs in some polypeptides.

b   α-Proteins

Although the diffraction patterns from naturally occurring materials such as hair, wool, porcupine quill and muscle are similar to those from synthetic α-polypeptides, there are important differences between them. In the diffraction patterns from the natural fibres, in

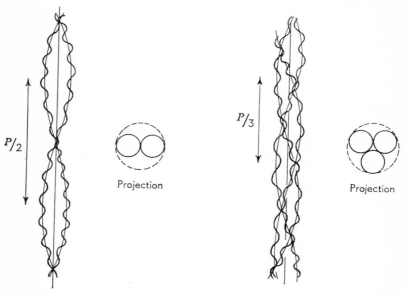

Fig. 3.5 A diagram of two-stranded and three-stranded coiled-coils. The diffracted intensity from such structures will depend on the structure of a single strand, on the number of strands, and on the directions of the strands relative to each other.

addition to the meridional reflection due to a periodicity of 1·5 Å, there is also a meridional reflection due to a periodicity of 5·1 Å, On the patterns from the synthetic fibres, the reflection due to a similar spacing occurs at 5·4 Å, and is off-meridional. One way of accounting for the 5·1 Å meridional reflection is to twist the α-helices round each other to form a coiled-coil. This was proposed by Crick (1952) and by Pauling and Corey (1953b). The α-helix then forms the minor helix of the coiled-coil, and the helical path of its axis follows the major helix.

The theory of diffraction by a coiled-coil was developed by Crick (1953a) and applied to calculate the Fourier transform of two- and

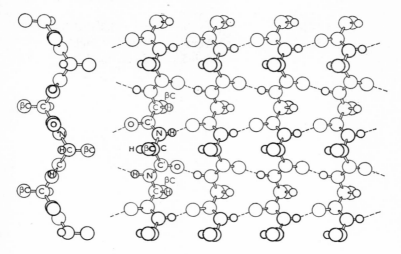

Fig. 3.6 A drawing of the parallel-chain pleated sheet. (From Pauling and Corey, 1951h.)

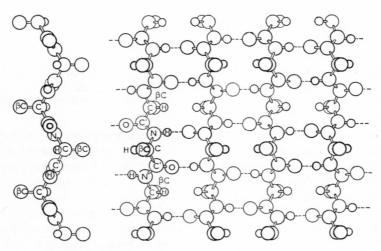

Fig. 3.7 A drawing of the antiparallel-chain pleated sheet. (From Pauling and Corey, 1951h.)

three-stranded coiled-coils of right-handed α-helices and a left-handed major helix of pitch 186 Å.

Cohen and Holmes (1943) have shown that a detailed interpretation of the diffraction pattern from a molluscan 'catch' muscle is possible in terms of a two-stranded coiled-coil model. The extra

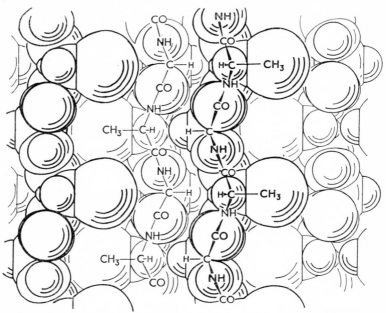

Fig. 3.8 A drawing showing the packing arrangement of antiparallel-chain pleated sheets in *Bombyx mori* fibrain, viewed perpendicular to the fibre axis and parallel to the plated sheets. (From Marsh, Corey and Pauling, 1955a.)

layer lines which the coiled-coil diffraction theory postulates are also resolved in the diffraction pattern. A similar analysis of the α-keratin pattern from porcupine quill tips has been made by Fraser, MacRae and Miller (1964), and the evidence suggests that the coiled-coil is probably three-stranded in this structure.

Crick (1953b) has proposed that the physical reason for coiled-coiling is the fact that it is then easier for the side groups of one α-helix to fit between the side groups of a neighbouring α-helix. By forming a coiled-coil, the number of residues per turn along the line of contact of two helices can be made equal to 3·5, which allows interlocking of side groups.

4   β-Structures

Structures in which the polypeptide chains are extended are referred to as β-structures. Astbury and Woods (1933) proposed that in β-keratin the extended polypeptide chains were bonded together to form sheets. This proposal was modified in detail by Pauling and Corey (1951h and 1953a) when they proposed the parallel-chain and antiparallel-chain pleated sheet models for the β-structures. In the parallel-chain sheets all the chains run in the same direction, while in the antiparallel-chain sheets, adjacent chains run in opposite directions.

There are three important periodicities in β-structures: the repeat distance along the polypeptide chain, the interchain spacing within a sheet, and the intersheet spacing. When the conformation of the chains are most favourable, the axial repeat distance in the parallel-chain model is 6·5 Å, and it is 7·0 Å in the antiparallel-chain model. These periodicities give rise to layer-lines, and because the chains have a two-fold screw axis there will be a meridional reflection on the second layer-line. The inter-chain spacing within sheets is about 4·7 Å, but the intersheet spacing depends on the size of the amino acid side groups and can vary between 3·5 and 8·0 Å.

The most common naturally occurring β-protein is fibroin from which silk fibres are composed. The silks that have been studied in most detail are those from *Bombyx mori* and from *Antherae mylitta* (Tussah silk). The structures in both these silks have been shown to be built up from antiparallel-chain pleated sheets (Marsh, Corey and Pauling, 1955a and b).

Bombyx silk is composed of 44% glycine, 29% alanine, 12% serine and 15% of other amino acids, and most of the chains in the Marsh *et al.* model have the sequence Gly·P·Gly·P, where P is either alanine or serine. This means that the hydrogen atoms of glycine protrude from one side of the sheet and the methyl and hydroxymethyl groups of alanine and serine from the other. The sheets pack together as illustrated in Fig. 3.9 with the side groups of one sheet fitting between similar groups of the adjacent sheet so that the distance between sheets are alternately 3·5 and 5·7 Å.

Due to the greater irregularity in the amino acid sequence in Tussah silk, the bulky side groups protrude on both sides of the pleated sheet, so that sheets are uniformly separated by a distance of 5·3 Å.

6

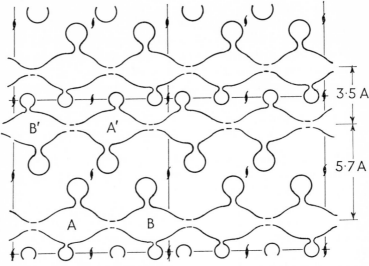

Fig. 3.9   The arrangement of the chains in *Bombyx mori* fibrain as seen in projection along the fibre axis. The large circles represent methyl groups and the small circles represent hydrogen atoms. (From Marsh, Corey and Pauling, 1955a.)

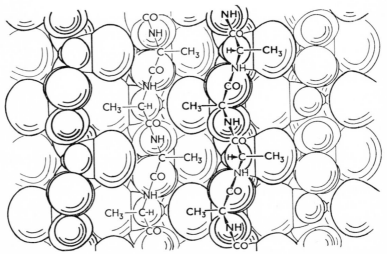

Fig. 3.10   A drawing showing the packing arrangement of antiparallel-chain pleated sheets in Tussah silk fibrain, viewed perpendicular to the fibre axis and parallel to the plated sheets. (From Marsh, Corey and Pauling, 1955b.)

Synthetic polypeptides can also exist in the β form, and a detailed analysis of β-PLA by Brown and Trotter (1956) shows that the best agreement with the observed diffracted intensity is obtained from a model in which the chain direction within a sheet is random. A detailed analysis of β-keratin by Fraser and MacRae (1962) shows that the same conclusions apply to this structure as to β-PLA.

5 Cross-β Structures

When fibres of the *k-m-e-f* group of proteins are immersed in hot water or placed in steam, supercontraction occurs. The x-ray

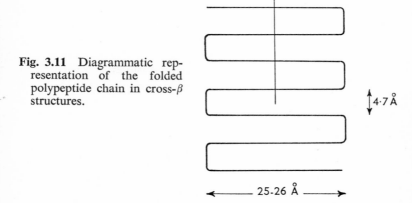

Fig. 3.11 Diagrammatic representation of the folded polypeptide chain in cross-β structures.

diffraction pattern from supercontracted fibres suggests that the polypeptide chains are in an extended conformation but with their axes perpendicular to the fibre axis, and the term cross-β was used by Astbury, Dickinson and Baily (1935) to describe the structure.

Recently, the cross-β structure has been shown to occur in the natural state. Rudall (Parker and Rudall, 1957; Rudall, 1962) has obtained cross-β diffraction patterns from the egg-stalk silk of the lace wing fly, *Chrysopa flava*. When the fibres are stretched, the x-ray diffraction pattern changes to that of the normal β-type pattern, which suggests that in the cross-β conformation, long polypeptide chains are folded back on themselves in the form of a Chinese cracker.

Cross-β x-ray diffraction patterns have also been obtained from certain synthetic polypeptides where the degree of polymerization is small (Bradbury *et al.*, 1960). It is believed that in these structures the short polypeptide chains form long micells with the chain axes perpendicular to the long axis of the micell. During the specimen preparation the micells become oriented with their long axes parallel to each other, so that the polypeptide chains are perpendicular to this direction. No secondary folding of the chain is thus envisaged in the synthetic polypeptides.

6   Collagen

Collagen is the fibrous protein which is found mainly in connective tissue and tendon. It is characterized by its unusual amino acid composition; nearly one-third of the residues are glycine, about 10% are proline, and about 8% are hydroxyproline. The C_δ atom in proline and hydroxyproline is bonded to the imino nitrogen so that the hydrogen bonds which occur in the α-helix and in the β sheets can not be formed.

Sequence analysis of dipeptides and tripeptides extracted from collagen suggests that every third residue in the polypeptide chain is glycine, and that the structure should accommodate the sequence —Gly·R_1·R_2—, where R_1 is proline or another amino acid, and R_2 is hydroxyproline or another amino acid.

a   Polyproline, polyglycine II and polyhydroxyproline

The x-ray diffraction patterns obtained by Cowan and McGavin (1955) from poly-L-proline were quite different from those from α and β structures. They interpreted the diffraction pattern as due to a left-handed helix of pitch 9·36 Å, and with three residues per turn of the helix.

A similar polypeptide chain conformation was proposed for polyglycine II by Crick and Rich (1955). Polyglycine can be precipitated from solution in two different forms. Polyglycine I gives a typical β-type x-ray diffraction pattern, but that from polyglycine II is quite different. In the structure proposed for polyglycine II by Crick and Rich, each residue was hydrogen bonded to a neighbouring chain (Fig. 3.13).

Poly-L-hydroxyproline has also been shown to have a similar chain conformation to that of poly-L-proline (Sasisekharan, 1959).

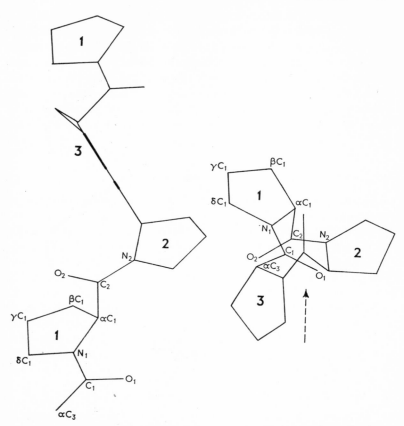

Fig. 3.12   Part of a single chain of poly-L-proline, viewed along the three-
fold axis (right), and perpendicular to this axis (left). (From Cowan
and McGavin, 1955.)

The chain conformation in these three synthetic polypeptides is
closely related to that proposed in collagen.

b Polypeptide chain conformation in collagen

The x-ray diffraction pattern from collagen is characteristic of
that from a helical structure (Cohen and Bear, 1953; Cowan, North
and Randall, 1953). By keeping the specimen under tension during
the exposure, Cowan *et al.* obtained greatly improved diffraction
patterns which facilitated their interpretation.

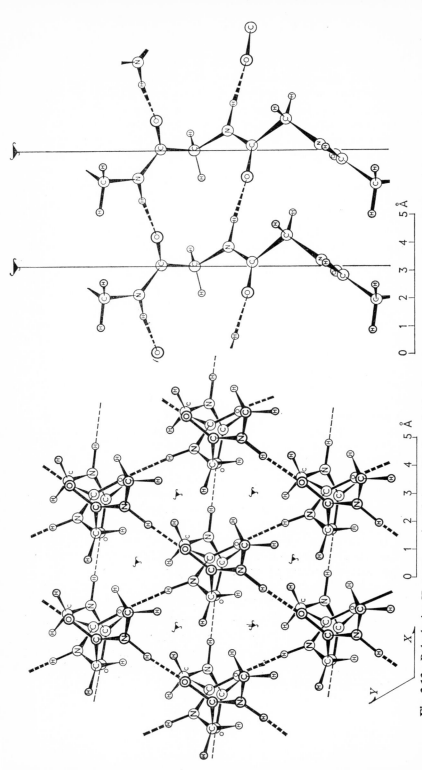

Fig. 3.13 Polyglycine II structure viewed down the three-fold axis and perpendicular to this axis. (From Crick and Rich, 1955.)

In 1954, Ramachandran and Kartha proposed that in collagen, three parallel, left-handed helical chains were hydrogen bonded together to form a unit. The pitch of each helix was 9·5 Å and there were three residues per turn of the helix. This model, however, could not account for the strong meridional reflection corresponding to a periodicity of 2·86 Å, and in order to overcome this drawback Ramachandran and Kartha (1955) proposed that the three helices of the earlier model should be non-integral, and twisted so as to form a three-stranded coiled-coil. In this new model, a left-handed minor helix with $3\frac{1}{3}$ residues per turn was made to form a right-handed major helix of pitch 85·8 Å and radius 2·5 Å, and with 30 residues per turn. The allowed sequence of amino acids along a chain in the model was —Gly·R·P—, where P is proline or hydroxyproline, and R is any other residue. For every three residues in the chain, two systematic hydrogen bonds were formed between chains.

The same basic three-stranded coiled-coil model for collagen was derived by Rich and Crick (1955) following their proposed structure for polyglycine II, but they criticized Ramachandran and Kartha's model on the grounds that it could not accommodate the sequence —Gly. Pro. Hypro.—. Rich and Crick proposed two possible models for collagen which they called collagen I and collagen II. The difference between them is in the sequence of hydrogen bonds between the three helices forming the coiled-coil. If we consider two helices of the unit of three forming the coiled-coil, then collagen I is formed by placing the third helix on one side of these two, and collagen II is formed by placing the third helix on the other side. If the chains are viewed in projection from the carboxyl ends, then in collagen I successive N—H . . . O hydrogen bonds point in an anticlockwise direction, and in collagen II they point in a clockwise direction. The evidence favours the collagen II model as the more likely form of the collagen molecule. In this model only one systematic hydrogen bond is formed for every three residues and the sequence —Gly·Pro·Hypro·— is allowed.

Cowan, McGavin and North (1955) also arrived at the same two forms of three-stranded coiled-coils for the collagen polypeptide chain, following their structure analysis of poly-L-proline.

From a survey of possible three-stranded coiled-coil models, Bear (1956) also arrived at the same two models as the other groups. Thus four groups of workers came to similar conclusions concerning the basic chain conformation in collagen.

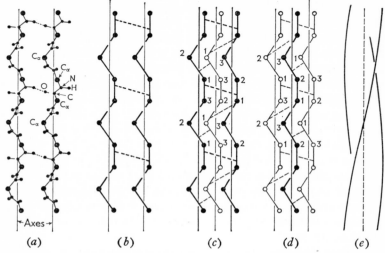

Fig. 3.14 A schematic drawing illustrating how the polypeptide chain conformation in collagen can be derived from the polyglycine II structure. (a) two chains from polyglycine II, (b) the same chains showing only the C_α atoms and the hydrogen bonds (dashed lines), (c) a third chain added behind the two chains in (h), which generates collagen I, (d) a third chain added in front of the two chains in (b) which produces collagen II. (e) In collagen, the three chains are twisted so as to form a coiled-coil. The sites numbered 1 in (c) and (d) are occupied by glycine. (From Rich and Crick, 1961.)

Details of the structure have yet to be finally established, although a refined model has been proposed by Ramachandran *et al.* (1962). The fact that synthetic poly(—Gly.Pro.Hypro.—) gives very similar x-ray diffraction patterns to those from collagen (Rogulenkova *et al.* 1964) may be important in deciding the final molecular model.

7 Low Angle Diffraction by Fibrous Proteins

Many fibrous proteins give low angle diffraction patterns, indicating the presence of large order periodicities in the specimens. The complete determination of fibrous protein structure must account for these large order periodicities, as well as the wide angle pattern which depends on the polypeptide chain conformation.

Low angle meridional reflections may arise from a regularly repeating sequence of amino acids along the chains, or may also arise due to a linear, or helical, arrangement of subunits within the fibre.

Low angle equatorial diffraction is due to the grouping of polypeptide chains to form larger units. The low angle x-ray diffraction studies of muscle fibres by Huxley (1951, 1952, 1953), combined with electron microscope, light microscope and chemical studies, were significant in the development of the sliding filament model of muscular action (Hanson and Huxley, 1955).

8 Globular Proteins

The sequence of amino acids along a polypeptide chain is called the primary structure of the chain. The secondary structure refers to the spatial relationship between adjacent residues along the chain, as, for example, in the α-helix. In the case of globular proteins the polypeptide chains are folded so as to form compact molecules, and the folded conformation is referred to as the tertiary structure of the chain. If a number of folded units form a larger organised structure, then the relative arrangement of these is called the quaternary structure of the molecule.

Many globular proteins can be extracted from cells and crystallized. In 1937, Bernal, Fankuchen and Perutz obtained single crystal diffraction patterns from haemoglobin, and the detailed study of this protein by Perutz and his co-workers culminated in the discovery that the isomorphous attachment of heavy atoms to the molecule could be used to determine its structure (Green, Ingram and Perutz, 1954). Application of the isomorphous replacement method to myoglobin by Kendrew and his co-workers resulted in the first structure determination of a globular protein (Kendrew *et al.*, 1958).

The molecular weights of globular proteins are of the order of tens of thousands, so that the structure determination is a very complex problem. About 40–60% of the volume of a protein crystal is occupied by the mother liquor from which the protein is crystallized. A small number of the solution molecules will be bound to the protein molecules, but most of them will be in a disordered liquid state filling the regions between the protein molecules. This means that the environment of the protein molecules in a crystal is not very different from that when it is in solution. This is important because it suggests that the conformation in the living cell, under physiological conditions, is similar to that in the crystal.

One of the main aims of x-ray structure analysis of proteins is to determine the factors that affect the tertiary structure. Evidence suggests that if folded polypeptide chains are unfolded and then allowed to fold up again, they will regain their original tertiary structure. Thus the sequence of amino acids appears to decide the tertiary structure. It is hoped that as more protein structures are determined in detail, general rules may emerge which will enable the tertiary structure to be predicted if the primary structure is known.

If a protein crystal is allowed to dry, it then collapses, and the arrangement of the molecules becomes disordered. For this reason, it is necessary to keep the crystal wet during the x-ray exposure. This is done by sealing the crystal in a thin-walled glass capillary tube which also contains a small amount of the mother liquor, although the crystal itself should not be covered with liquid. Protein crystals under such conditions give x-ray diffraction patterns with reflections often extending to regions corresponding to spacings of 2 Å or less. In between the extreme wet and dry states of protein crystals there are sometimes well defined shrinkage stages when the unit cell dimensions change sharply with variation in humidity as the crystal goes from one stage to another.

Because of lack of information about the phases of the diffracted spectra, most of the early protein work involved the calculation of Patterson functions. However, the complexity of the Patterson maps made it obvious that, in order to determine protein structures, the phases of the structure factors would have to be determined first.

Haemoglobin had been studied extensively before it was discovered that the isomorphous method could be used as a phase determining method. From a study of crystals containing different concentrations of salt solution surrounding the molecules, and from considerations of molecular packing arrangements, Bragg and Perutz (1952a and b) concluded that the shape of the haemoglobin molecule was ellipsoidal and of size $71 \times 53 \times 53$ Å.

Also, from the earlier studies, Bragg and Perutz (1952c) had determined the phases of many of the spectra in the centrosymmetric *h0l* zone of reflection by comparing the intensities of the various shrinkage stages of haemoglobin crystals. This was a particularly elegant method which utilized the lattice changes to sample the Fourier transform of the molecule at different points, and enable the continuous transform, and hence the phases, to be determined.

While the method could be applied to a centrosymmetric projection where the phases are either 0 or 180°, its extension to three dimensions would be difficult because the phases may then have any value.

With the discovery by Green, Ingram and Perutz (1954) that crystals of horse haemoglobin to which heavy atoms had been attached were isomorphous with crystals of the native protein, and showed measurable changes in the intensities of the diffraction spectra, the way was open to make a direct determination of the phases. The native horse haemoglobin molecule contains four sulphydryl groups, and when haemoglobin was crystallized in the presence of parachloro-mercuri-benzoate (PCMB), or in the presence of silver ions, two of the sulphydryl groups combined with PCMB groups or silver ions. The x and z co-ordinates of the heavy atoms were determined from a difference Patterson synthesis calculated for the centrosymmetric projection. The signs determined for the reflections confirmed those determined by the Fourier transform method and resolved the ambiguities of that method. Using the phases determined for the $h0l$ reflections, Bragg and Perutz (1954) calculated the Fourier synthesis for the b-axis projection of haemoglobin. This projection, however, contained all the atoms in a thickness of about 60 Å and the overlap was too great to show any details of the structure. It was then obvious that the method should be extended to three dimensions. This was first done successfully for the smaller myoblobin molecule.

9 Myoglobin

Myoglobin has a molecular weight of about 17,000, and consists of a single polypeptide chain of 153 amino acid residues and one haem group. The haem group, which is also found in haemoglobin, is composed of four five-membered rings linked together in a planar arrangement, with an iron atom centrally situated between the four rings. The function of myolgobin is to store oxygen in muscle tissue and it is found in particularly high concentrations in the muscles of diving mammals such as whale and seal. The myoglobin studied by Kendrew was that from sperm whale, and it crystallizes in a monoclinic cell with

$$a = 64\cdot6\ \text{Å}, \qquad b = 31\cdot3\ \text{Å}, \qquad c = 34\cdot8\ \text{Å}, \qquad \beta = 105\cdot5°$$

and in the space group $P2_1$.

When oxygen combines with myoglobin it is linked to the iron atom and in the absence of oxygen a water molecule is probably attached to the iron atom at this position. When the protein is combined with oxygen it is referred to as oxymyoglobin and when it is free of oxygen it is called reduced myoglobin, although in both cases the iron atom is in the ferrous state. In air, the iron atom is readily oxidized to the ferric state and the protein is then called metmyoglobin. It was the structure of sperm whale metmyoglobin that was determined by Kendrew.

Myoglobin does not contain the sulphydryl groups which are found in haemoglobin, and attempts to form derivatives, in which the heavy atom groups were attached to the haem group, were unsuccessful because they were unstable. The procedure used to prepare suitable heavy atom derivatives, therefore, was an empirical one of crystallizing myoglobin in the presence of heavy atom groups, taking x-ray diffraction photographs, and comparing these with the patterns from native myoglobin. When measurable differences in intensity were observed, these were used to calculate difference Patterson syntheses from which the suitability of the derivative could be ascertained. For a suitable derivative, the number of heavy atom sites per asymmetric unit should be small and the degree of occupancy of the sites should be high.

The first myoglobin derivatives were prepared by crystallizing sperm whale myoglobin from ammonium sulphate solution in the presence of mercuri-iodide ions (HgI_4^{--}). Other suitable derivatives were those containing gold tetrachloride ions ($AuCl_4^-$), silver ions, mercury diammine ($HgAm_2$) and p-chloromercuribenzene sulphonate (PCMBS). In addition to the single heavy atom derivatives, double derivatives were obtained with PCMBS + $HgAm_2$ and with PCMBS + $AuCl_4^-$.

The procedure used in the isomorphous replacement method of phase determination has already been given. When the phases are known, a Fourier synthesis is calculated and the structure of the molecule should appear in the Fourier maps.

The three-dimensional analysis of myoglobin has been carried out in three stages. In the first stage, the analysis was made at a resolution of 6 Å using only the 400 reflection on the diffraction patterns which correspond to spacings equal to and greater than this value (Kendrew *et al.*, 1958; Bodo *et al.*, 1959). The second stage was carried out at a resolution of 2 Å (Kendrew *et al.*, 1960 and 1961), and involved about 10,000 reflections. The third stage involves about 25,000 reflections and gives a resolution of 1·4 Å and it has enabled most of the 1260 non-hydrogen atoms in the structure to be located (Kendrew, 1963).

The 6 Å resolution Fourier synthesis of myoglobin revealed the haem group as a disc-like structure, and the polypeptide chain as containing many rod-like regions joined by irregular regions. The tertiary structure appeared to be very complex and in certain regions it was difficult to trace the chain along the molecule unambiguously because of the low electron density at some of the bends. The straight rod-like regions of the model suggested an α-helical conformation, but higher resolution was required to prove this conclusively.

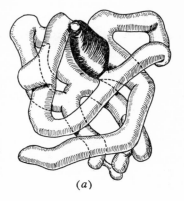

(a)

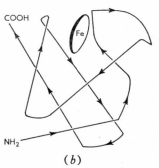

(b)

Extension of the analysis to a resolution of 2 Å was an immense task, involving the measurement of about 10,000 reflections from the native crystal and the same number from each of four heavy atom derivatives. The phases of the structure factors were calculated on a high speed digital computer.

Although individual atoms were not revealed at a resolution of 2 Å, the 2 Å Fourier synthesis showed the haem group very clearly, as well as the secondary structure of most of the polypeptide chain, together with the shape of most of

Fig. 3.15 (a) Model of the myoglobin molecule derived from the 6 Å Fourier synthesis.
(b) The course of the polypeptide chain as deduced from the 2 Å Fourier synthesis. (From Kendrew *et al.*, 1960.)

the amino acid side groups. The orientation of the haem group was in agreement with that derived from electron spin resonance studies (Ingram and Kendrew, 1956), and it was apparent that it was linked to a helical region of the polypeptide chain through a histidine residue.

The straight rod-like regions of the 6 Å resolution model were now observed to be hollow, with a high electron density following a helical path with a pitch of 5·4 Å, which was in agreement with a right-handed α-helical conformation of polypeptide chain.

Although individual atoms in the amino acids along the chain could not be resolved, the electron density distribution at 2 Å

Fig. 3.16 The electron density distribution in the plane of the haem group in the 2 Å Fourier synthesis of myoglobin. The atomic arrangement in the haem group is shown superposed on the electron density. (From Kendrew *et al.*, 1960.)

0 1 2 3 4 Å

resolution often enabled the side group to be identified unambiguously (Kendrew *et al.*, 1961), and about half of the side groups were identified with certainty. Chemical analysis of the amino acid sequence along parts of the sperm whale myoglobin chain had been made by Edmundson and Hirs (1961) and by combining the chemical and x-ray results the positions of two-thirds of the amino acid residues were known with a high degree of certainty. Another one-fifth of the residues were probably correct but identification of the remainder was uncertain.

The 1·4 Å resolution analysis of myoglobin, together with more detailed chemical analysis, have enabled about 120 amino acids to be known with certainty and many of the others with a high degree of probability (Kendrew, 1963). Intensity data for the 1·4 Å analysis were collected by means of an automatic linear diffractometer (Arndt and Phillips, 1961).

The procedure used in the 1·4 Å analysis is different from that used in the 6 Å and 2 Å analysis. Myoglobin contains 1260 atoms (excluding hydrogen atoms) and the position of 825 of these were known from the 2 Å analysis. The phases of all the structure factors were calculated on the basis of the atoms in known positions, and these calculated phases were used with the observed amplitudes to calculate a Fourier synthesis. Such a synthesis should show the atoms used in the phase calculations in improved positions and also some of the atoms which were not included. The new atoms which are revealed in the Fourier synthesis can then be used to calculate new phases from which a new Fourier synthesis can be calculated. The first cycle of refinement for myoglobin included 825 atoms, and the second cycle included 925 atoms (Kendrew, 1963). Successive cycles should eventually reveal all the atoms in the molecule.

The model derived from the x-ray analysis of myoglobin shows that more than two-thirds of the polypeptide chain is in the α-helical conformation. The remainder of the chain is non-helical and forms the bends and corners of the chain. The four proline residues in myoglobin occur at bends or non-helical regions, as might be expected, although there are other bends where proline is not present. There is a tendency for the polar side groups to be on the outside of the molecule and for non-polar ones to lie on the inside of the molecule.

(a)

(b)

Fig. 3.17 (a) A cylindrical projection of a helical segment of a polypeptide chain in the 2 Å Fourier synthesis of myoglobin, with a projection of the α-helix superposed.
(b) A diagram showing the atoms in (a). The points marked β and β' correspond to alternative positions of the C_β atom. β is the position for a right-handed, and β' that for a left-handed helix of L-amino acids. (From Kendrew *et al.*, 1960).

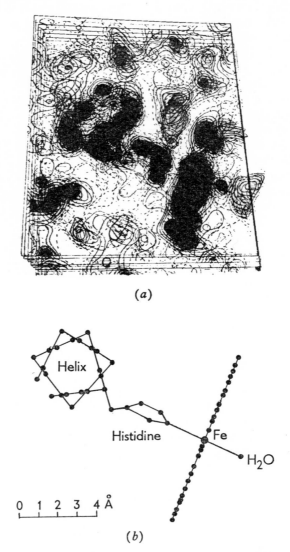

(a)

(b)

Fig. 3.18 A diagram showing how the haem group, viewed edge-on, is linked to a helical region of the polypeptide chain through a histidine residue in myoglobin. This was derived from the 3-dimensional Fourier synthesis at 2 Å resolution, a view of which is shown in (a). (From Kendrew *et al.*, 1960.)

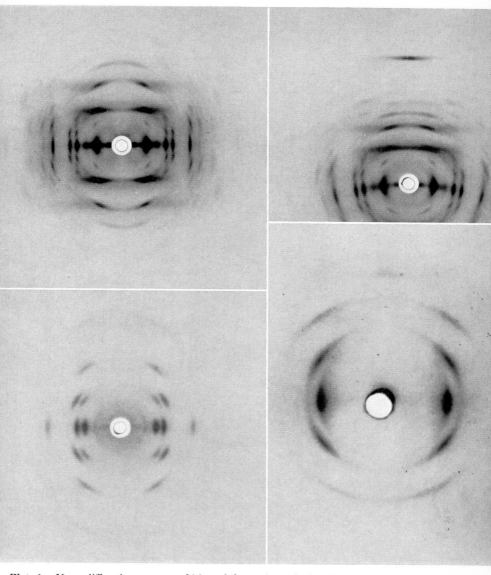

Plate 1. X-ray diffraction patterns of (a) *top left:* α poly-L-alanine, fibre axis vertical (Bamford *et al.*, 1954), (b) *top right:* α poly-L-alanine, fibre axis inclined so that the meridional reflection corresponding to a spacing of 1·495 Å is recorded (Brown and Trotter, 1956), (c) *bottom left:* β poly-L-alanine (Bamford *et al.*, 1954), (d) *bottom right:* poly-L-proline (courtesy of Dr. Pauline Harrison).

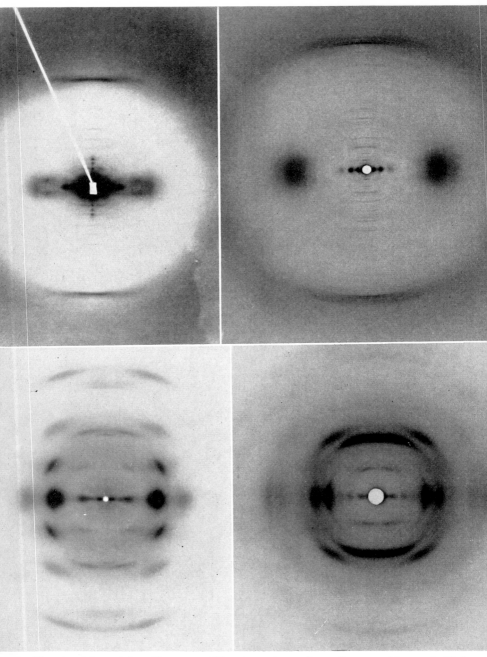

Plate 2. (a) *top left:* α-Type x-ray diffraction pattern of a molluscan catch muscle (Cohen and Holmes, 1963). (b) *top right:* X-ray diffraction pattern of α-keratin of porcupine quill (courtesy of Drs. R. D. B. Fraser, T. P. MacRae and A. Miller). (c) *bottom left:* β-Type x-ray diffraction pattern from *Bombyx mori* silk (Marsh, Corey and Pauling, 1955a). (d) *bottom right:* Cross-β type x-ray diffraction pattern from *Chrysopa flava* egg-stalk silk (courtesy of Dr. K. M. Rudall).

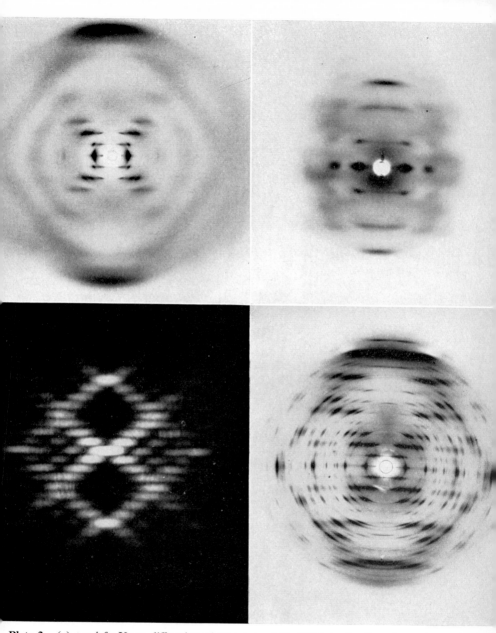

Plate 3. (a) *top left:* X-ray diffraction photograph of Na DNA in the *B* conformation at 92% relative humidity. (b) *top right:* X-ray diffraction photograph of Li DNA in the *B* conformation at 66% relative humidity (Langridge *et al.*, 1960) (c) *bottom left:* Optical diffraction pattern from projections of a row of atoms on a helix. There are eight atoms per turn of the helix (Stokes, 1955b). (d) *bottom right:* X-ray diffraction photograph of collagen (courtesy of Dr. A. C. T. North).

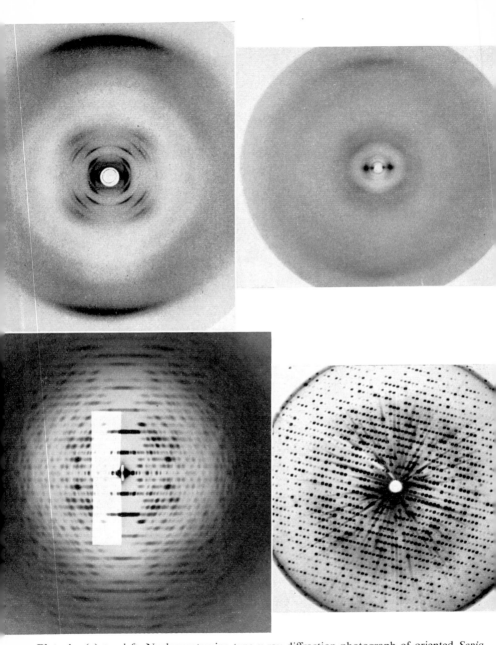

Plate 4. (a) *top left:* Nucleoprotamine type x-ray diffraction photograph of oriented *Sepia* sperm. (b) *top right:* X-ray diffraction photograph of extracted calf thymus nucleohistone fibres at 98% relative humidity (Wilkins, Zubay and Wilson, 1959). (c) *bottom left:* X-ray diffraction photograph of oriented tobacco mosaic virus gel (courtesy of Dr. K. C. Holmes). (d) *bottom right:* X-ray diffraction photograph of a single-crystal of myoglobin taken on a precession camera (courtesy of Dr. J. C. Kendrew).

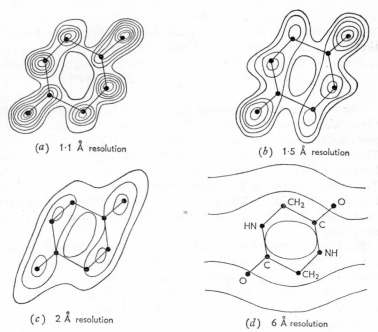

(*a*) 1·1 Å resolution

(*b*) 1·5 Å resolution

(*c*) 2 Å resolution

(*d*) 6 Å resolution

Fig. 3.19 A section of the three dimensional electron density distribution of diketopiperazine calculated at various degrees of resolution. Although all the atoms are not resolved at 2 Å resolution, the shape of the molecule is apparent. (From Hodgkin, 1960.)

10   Haemoglobin

Haemoglobin has a molecular weight of about 65,000 and consists of four polypeptide chains and four haem groups. The four chains, which are identical in pairs, are referred to as α-and β-chains, and they are approximately the same size. Thus the molecule consists of two α-chains, two β-chains and four haem groups.

The x-ray analysis of haemoglobin has not yet been carried out to the same resolution as myoglobin, but the three-dimensional analysis at 5·5 Å resolution (Perutz *et al.*, 1960, Cullis *et al.*, 1961 and 1962) were detailed enough to show the arrangement of the polypeptide chains and to enable interesting comparisons with the structure of myoglobin to be made.

The function of haemoglobin is to transport oxygen in the blood stream, and the red colour of blood is due to haemoglobin molecules. The haemoglobin used by Perutz was that from horse and it was in the oxy- or methaemoglobin form. The molecules crystallize in space group C2 with half a molecule forming the asymmetric unit. The unit cell dimensions are a = 108·95 Å, b = 63·51 Å, c = 54·92 Å, β = 110°53′.

The 5·5 Å resolution Fourier synthesis of haemoglobin showed the conformation of the four polypeptide chains and showed how remarkably similar this conformation was to the myoglobin chain. The two α- and two β-chains are arranged approximately tetrahedrally to form the quaternary structure of the whole molecule. The α-chain contains 141 amino acid residues and the β-chain contains 146 residues. The extra five residues in the β-chain have been correlated with a structural difference at one particular loop in the chain.

The x-ray analysis (Perutz *et al.*, 1960) shows that the haem groups are quite far from each other. The closest distance between iron atoms is 25·2 Å, and between symmetrically related pairs the distances are 33·4 and 36·0 Å. This was a surprising result because the rate at which oxygen combines with a haem group increases when oxygen atoms are already attached to other haem groups, which suggests some interaction between them. The haem-haem interaction may thus be transmitted via the polypeptide chains.

Oxygen-free haemoglobin, referred to as reduced haemoglobin has different physical properties to oxyhaemoglobin, so that a comparison of the two structures is of great interest. An analysis of human reduced haemoglobin showed that the form of the polypeptide chains was very similar to that in horse oxyhaemoglobin, but the separation of the β-chains was greater by 7 Å (Perutz and Muirhead, 1962). Conclusive proof that this difference was due to the state of oxygenation, rather than a difference in structure between the two haemoglobins, was supplied by the analysis of reduced horse haemoglobin, where it was shown that the β-chains had moved apart by 7 Å (Perutz *et al.*, 1964). These studies illustrate how it may eventually be possible to explain some biological processes in terms of structural changes at the molecular level.

11   Other Globular Proteins

Although many crystalline globular proteins are under investigation at present, few have yet been carried to the stage where it is possible to draw many conclusions about the conformation of the polypeptide chains. The polypeptide chains in both myoglobin and haemoglobin have a large fraction in the α-helical conformation, whereas in many other globular proteins the fraction is much less. This makes it more difficult to interpret the Fourier syntheses at the resolution which was possible for myoglobin and haemoglobin. This was the case for chymotrypsinogen (Kraut *et al.*, 1962 and 1964) and for lysozyme (Blake *et al.*, 1962; Stanford *et al.*, 1962; Dickerson *et al.*, 1962). However, if suitable isomorphous derivatives are available, and if the diffraction patterns extend to regions corresponding to low spacings, interpretation of Fourier syntheses should be possible at higher resolution. Thus, at the time of writing, the structure of lysozyme, where the α-helix content of the molecule is only about 40%, has been determined by D. C. Phillips and his co-workers at the Royal Institution, London, by carrying out the analysis at 2 Å resolution.

4, Nucleic Acids

1 General Introduction

Nucleic acids are long polymers of nucleotides which play a fundamental part in the functioning of living cells. A nucleotide is composed of three components; a base, a sugar and a phosphate group. The sugar component is either D-ribose or 2'-deoxy D-ribose and this enables the nucleic acids to be divided into two groups, ribose nucleic acid (RNA) and deoxyribose nucleic acid (DNA).

Four commonly occurring bases are found in both DNA and RNA. Two of these are purines and the other two are pyrimidines. In both DNA and RNA the purine bases are adenine and guanine. The pyrimidine bases in DNA are cytosine and thymine and in RNA they are cytosine and uracil. Small quantities of other bases are found in some nucleic acids but they only differ slightly from the four common ones.

DNA and RNA can be extracted from cells by chemical methods and the extracted material can be studied by various chemical and physical techniques. Chemical studies (see Brown and Todd, 1955) have shown that the phosphate group of one nucleotide is linked to the sugar of the next nucleotide, so that the backbone of the polymer is a regular sequence of phosphate and sugar groups. The bases may be considered as side groups attached to the regular backbone, but the order in which they occur along the molecule is not known.

DNA is believed to be the carrier of the hereditary characteristics from one generation to the next. In the cell it is combined with

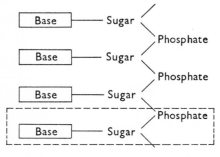

Fig. 4.1 Schematic formula of nucleic acid chains.

94

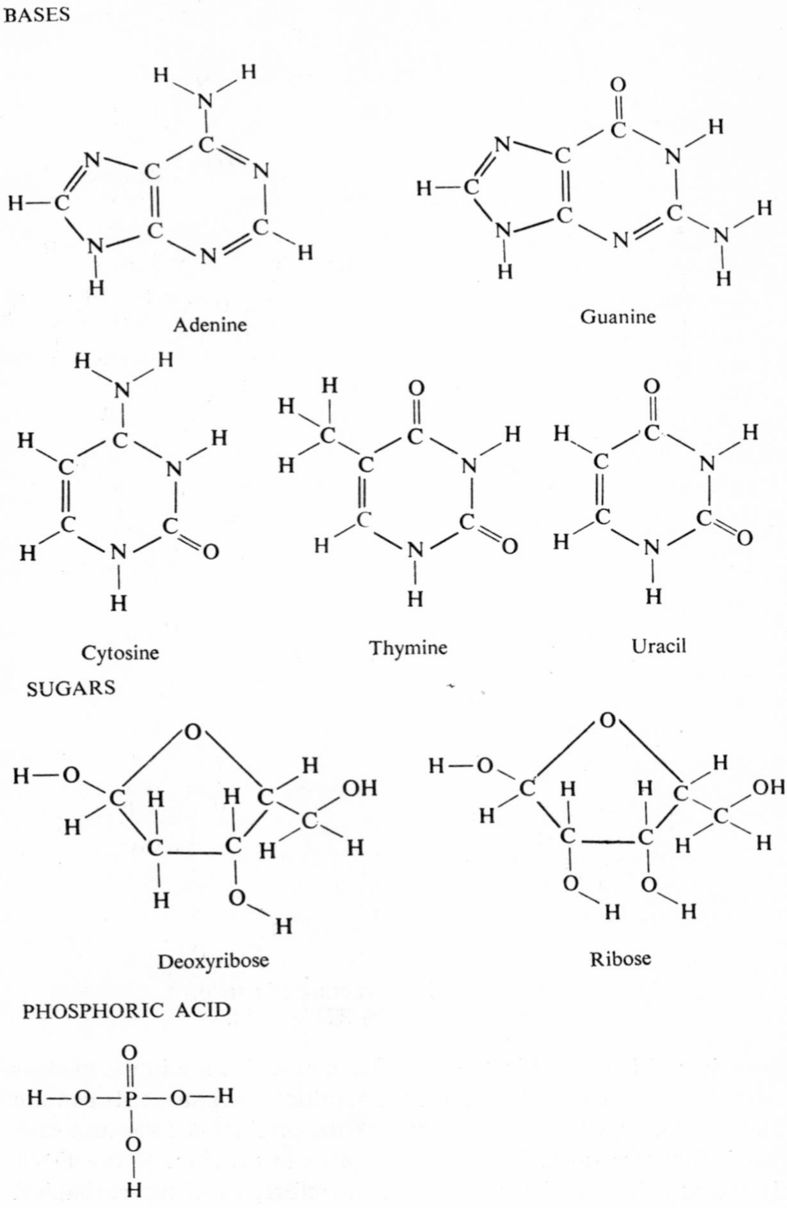

BASES

Adenine

Guanine

Cytosine

Thymine

Uracil

SUGARS

Deoxyribose

Ribose

PHOSPHORIC ACID

Fig. 4.2 Chemical structure of nucleic acid components.

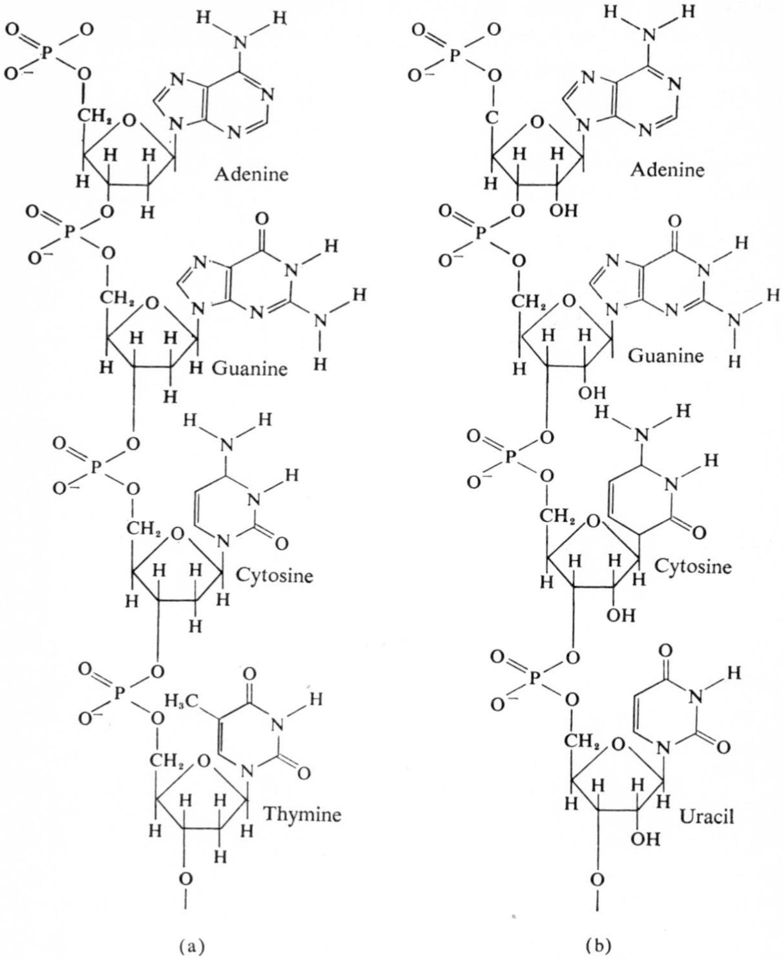

Fig. 4.3 Chemical structure of part of
(a) DNA chain, (b) RNA chain.

protein and is located in the chromosomes which are in the nucleus of the cell. When a cell divides, the resulting daughter cells contain the same number of chromosomes as the original cell because each original chromosome has replicated prior to division. If the DNA is the genetic material, there must, therefore, be some mechanism whereby it can replicate itself.

If the DNA is the genetic material it must also control the functioning of the living cell. It is believed to do this by determining which protein molecules are synthesized in the cell and by determining the sequence of amino acids along each of these. There is evidence that the information that enables it to do this is contained in the sequence of bases along the DNA. The problem of how four different bases can determine the sequence of amino acids along a

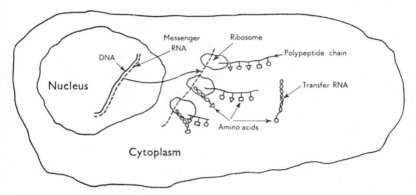

Fig. 4.4 Schematic diagram of protein synthesis.

protein molecule is known as the 'coding' problem, and the evidence at present is in favour of a triplet code whereby a sequence of three bases codes for one amino acid.

RNA plays an important role in the process of protein synthesis. The information contained in the DNA molecule is believed to be copied by messenger RNA which is built up along the DNA molecule in a specific manner, and, therefore, will have a base sequence related to that of the DNA. The messenger RNA goes out of the nucleus and attaches itself to ribosome particles in the cytoplasm. These are composed of protein and RNA, and this RNA is referred to as ribosomal RNA. A third kind of RNA, namely transfer RNA, has the function of bringing amino acids along to the ribosomes. The transfer RNA attaches itself to the messenger RNA in a specific manner, determined by the coding triplet, and the amino acids are then linked together to form a protein molecule.

This brief and simplified outline of the process of protein synthesis is given in order to illustrate the relationship between the various kinds of nucleic acid molecules. In addition to the messenger, ribosomal and transfer RNAs, there is the RNA found in viruses, referred to as viral RNA.

2   Nucleic Acid Components

Nucleic acids can be broken down into nucleotides, into nucleosides (a base attached to a sugar), and further still into their various

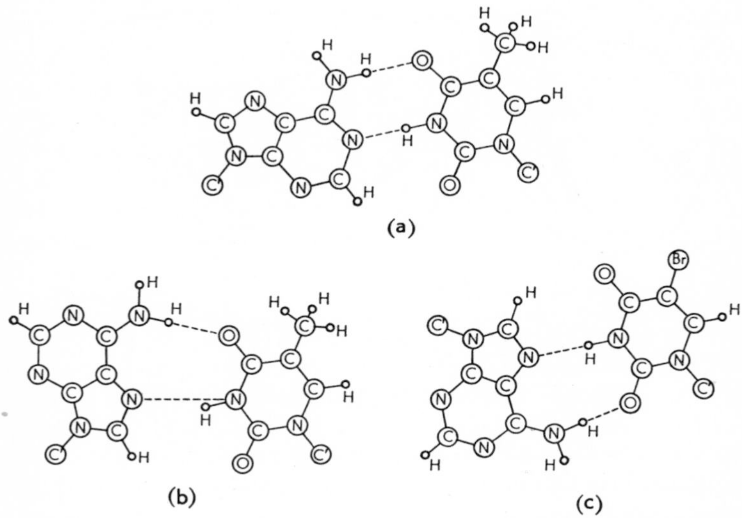

(a)

(b)   (c)

Fig. 4.5   Adenine-Thymine base-pairs
(a) Watson-Crick hydrogen bonding scheme as proposed for DNA.
(b) As found by Hoogsteen in a mixed crystal of 1-methylthymine and 9-methyladenine.
(c) As found by Haschemeyer and Sobell in a mixed crystal of adenosine and 5-bromouridine.

components. These breakdown products can be crystallized and their structure investigated by single crystal x-ray analysis. From the study of these components, accurate values of the bond lengths and angles are obtained, and also information about hydrogen bond formation.

Recently, a number of crystals have been studied which contain hydrogen bonded complexes of bases and of nucleosides. The first complex to be studied was one between 1-methyl-thymine and 9-methyladenine (Hoogsteen, 1959). This investigation showed that the hydrogen bonds between the two molecules were not the same as those proposed between adenine and thymine in DNA. This led to further studies of other complexes involving adenine and thymine as well as those involving guanine and cytosine.

Complexes between 9-ethyl guanine and 1-methylcytosine (O'Brien, 1963) and between 9-ethyl guanine and 1-methyl-5-bromocytosine (Sobell, Tomita and Rich, 1963) show the same hydrogen bonding schemes as proposed in DNA.

Studies of complexes between adenosine and 5-bromouridine (Haschemeyer and Sobell, 1963) and between 9-ethyl adenine and 1-methyl uracil (Mathews and Rich, 1964), however, revealed a third type of hydrogen bonding system which was different from that proposed for DNA and also from that found in Hoogsteen's structure.

Further studies of such complexes may indicate why certain hydrogen bonding schemes are found in particular circumstances.

3 Deoxyribose Nucleic Acid (DNA)

DNA has a molecular weight of several million. It can be extracted from the cell in the form of a salt. This material is fibrous and gives a characteristic x-ray diffraction pattern. Astbury and Bell (1938), who carried out the pioneer x-ray diffraction studies of DNA, interpreted the strong meridional reflection corresponding to a periodicity of 3·4 Å as being due to flat nucleotides stacked on top of each other to form a long molecule. At this time no studies of DNA components had been made.

In 1950 Furberg determined the structure of cytidine, which showed that the ribose and cytosine base were not coplanar but were closer to being at right angles to each other. Furberg (1952) incorporated this information in a modification of Astbury's DNA model when he considered possible DNA structures in the form of single helical polynucleotide chains.

Riley and Oster (1951) studied the effect of water content on unoriented DNA specimens and showed that over a particular range of water content the diffraction rings became very sharp, indicating that the crystallinity of the DNA specimen was dependent on the amount of water present.

The important experimental advance in the study of DNA structure came with Wilkin's discovery that it was possible to pull thin fibres from a concentrated DNA gel, and that if they were kept moist during an x-ray exposure, the quality of the x-ray diffraction patterns was greatly superior to that of those obtained previously. The fibres were 1–100 microns in diameter and showed sharp extinction between crossed polaroids. They were kept moist during the x-ray exposure by regulating the humidity in the x-ray camera. By varying the humidity it was discovered that the DNA structure changed from a highly crystalline form at 75% relative humidity, called the *A* form, to a semi-crystalline *B* form at 92% relative humidity.

A number of important results emerged from these x-ray studies. Firstly, DNAs extracted from different sources, although differing in base composition, gave essentially identical diffraction patterns.

Secondly, the diffraction pattern of the *B* form showed characteristic features of that due to a helical molecule.

Thirdly, the sharpness of the x-ray diffraction pattern of the *A* form of DNA showed that the molecules were highly regular and could pack together in a crystalline arrangement.

Further information about DNA came from other physical and chemical studies. The base composition of DNAs from different sources vary over a wide range, but Chargaff (1950) made the important discovery that the molar ratios of adenine to thymine and of guanine to cytosine were always close to unity.

Electrotitrometric studies of DNA showed that the bases were hydrogen bonded together, and flow-birefringence measurements, as well as the x-ray results, showed that the bases were perpendicular to the length of the DNA molecule. Electron microscope studies showed that the DNA molecules were threadlike and uniform, with a diameter of $\sim$20 Å.

This was the situation in 1953 when Watson and Crick (1953a) proposed a structure for DNA which explained the chemical analyses, was also in agreement with the x-ray diffraction results, and, moreover, had important biological implications. This elegant proposal has proved to be one of the most fruitful ideas in the history of biology.

Watson and Crick arrived at the structure by building accurate molecular models. They found that it was possible to build a double helical molecule of DNA in which the phosphate and deoxyribose groups were on the outside of the molecule and the two chains were hydrogen bonded together in a specific manner through the bases.

If adenine was hydrogen bonded to thymine, and guanine to cytosine, as shown in Fig. 4.6, then the distance between the C_1' atoms of the sugars was the same for the two base pairs, and all the glycosidic bonds made the same angle with the line joining the C_1' atoms as shown. This meant that the separation of the two sugar-phosphate chains was the same for both base pairs and the outer part of the molecule was perfectly regular. In the model, the sugar-phosphate

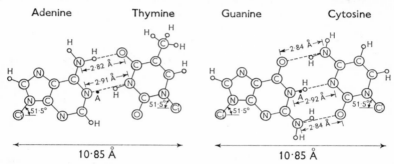

Adenine   Thymine   Guanine   Cytosine

10·85 Å   10·85 Å

Fig. 4.6   The two Watson-Crick base-pairs. A is the position of the helix axis in *B* DNA.

parts of the two polynucleotide chains were related by a two-fold axis perpendicular to the helix axis, which meant that the two polynucleotide chains were antiparallel.

Although the outside of the molecule was regular, any sequence of bases could occur along a polynucleotide chain, but the postulated specific pairing of bases meant that the bases on one chain would be related to those on the other. The two chains were thus complementary to each other.

The proposed specific pairing of bases was the most important feature of the Watson-Crick DNA structure because it suggested a way in which the molecule could replicate itself (Watson and Crick, 1953b). It was suggested that when the two complementary chains of a DNA molecule separated, each would act as a template for the production of new molecules. New complementary chains would build up along the two chains of the old molecule by specific pairing of bases so that two new molecules would be produced, identical to each other and to the original molecule.

Wilkins, Stokes and Wilson (1953), and Franklin and Gosling (1953a) showed that the Watson-Crick model was in general agreement with the x-ray diffraction data from the *B* form of DNA.

Shortly afterwards, Franklin and Gosling (1953b), and Wilkins, Seeds, Stokes and Wilson (1953) showed that the same basic structure could also explain the *A* DNA x-ray patterns.

The subsequent detailed analysis of the x-ray diffraction data from three different forms of DNA by Wilkins and his co-workers has shown that the basic Watson-Crick model is correct, although

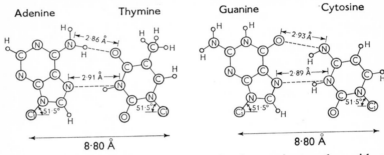

Fig. 4.7 The Hoogsteen adenine-thymine base pair, together with a guanine-cytosine base-pair of the same overall dimensions. The cytosine is required to exist in the imino (N—H) rather than the more common amino (N—H$_2$) form in order to produce this guanine-cytosine base-pair. (Data from Arnott et al., 1965.)

it had to be modified in detail (Langridge *et al.*, 1960a, b; Marvin *et al.*, 1961; Fuller *et al.*, 1965). The fact that it is possible to build a DNA model, which, by suitable changes in conformation, will fit the x-ray data for three different forms is much stronger evidence for the correctness of the basic structure than if only one form were studied.

a The B conformation

DNA occurs in the *B* conformation *in vivo* in sperm heads, when it is combined with protamine, and also in nucleohistone. There is also evidence that DNA exists in this conformation in dilute aqueous solutions. The *B* conformation is found in fibres of Li, Na, K and Rb salts of DNA at 92% relative humidity. The diffraction patterns from these fibres are rather diffuse, with only a few sharp reflections, indicating a semi-crystalline structure in the fibres. They are, however, highly characteristic of that expected from a helical structure with 10 residues per turn of a helix of pitch 34 Å.

Li DNA remains in the *B* conformation at lower humidities, and at 66% relative humidity it crystallizes in an orthorhombic unit cell with a $= 22\cdot7$, b $= 31\cdot2$ and c $= 33\cdot7$ Å, and sharp reflections are obtained on the x-ray fibre diffraction patterns. This makes it suitable for detailed analysis, and by using high resolution x-ray cameras it is possible to reduce the overlap of the reflection and in this way obtain three-dimensional intensity data.

The method which was initially used to determine the Li *B* DNA structure was that of accurate model building combined with Fourier transform calculations. Systematic changes were made in the model until good agreement was obtained between the observed and calculated transforms.

As the sequence of bases along the molecule is not known, the co-ordinates of an 'average' base were used in the calculations. The large amount of water in the structure was regarded as uniformly filling the space between the DNA molecules and the scattering factors of the atoms were modified to take this into account.

Eventually a stage was reached when it was difficult to improve the agreement, and at this stage Wilkins and his co-workers applied Fourier synthesis methods, using the

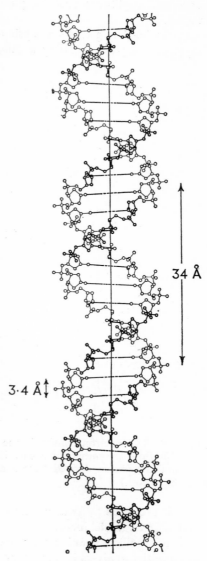

Fig. 4.8 The *B* DNA structure. The two chains are antiparallel and are hydrogen bonded together through the bases.

observed amplitudes and the phases derived from the molecular model.

Following Hoogsteen's analysis of the 9-methyladenine-1-methythymine complex, revealing a different hydrogen bonding system

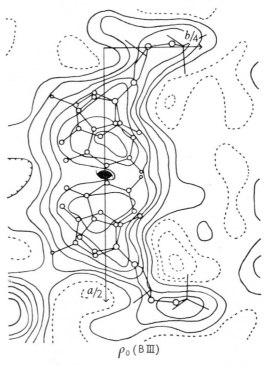

$\rho_0\,(B\,III)$

Fig. 4.9 The electron density in the plane of a base-pair in Li DNA. The Fourier synthesis was calculated using the observed amplitudes and the phases derived from a molecular model. (Courtesy of Dr. S. Arnott.)

to that proposed by Watson and Crick, Langridge and Rich (1960) built a DNA model incorporating the Hoogsteen base-pair, together with a modified guanine-cystosine pair of the same dimensions. The Fourier analyses by Arnott *et al.* (1965), however, have shown that the DNA model with Watson-Crick base-pairs is in better agreement with the experimental data than one with Hoogsteen-type base pairs.

b The A conformation

The *A* conformation exists in fibres of Na, K and Rb DNA, when the relative humidity of the surrounding atmosphere is 75%. The fibres are highly crystalline and the diffraction patterns are very detailed. The unit cell is monoclinic with a = 22·1, b = 40·4, c = 28·1 Å and β = 97·1°. In the *A* conformation there are 11 nucleotide pairs per turn of the helix of pitch 28 Å, and the base pairs are tilted 20° from perpendicular to the helix axis.

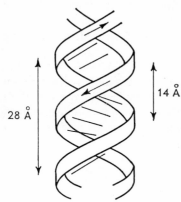

28 Å

14 Å

Fig. 4.10 Schematic representation of the *A* DNA structure.

18 Å

Base composition variation does not affect the *A* conformation, and the sodium salt of DNA from a wide variety of sources can adopt this conformation. However, NaDNA from two bacteriophages do not adopt the *A* conformation, but remain in the *B* conformation at 75% relative humidity. Both these DNAs contain glucose residues attached to some of the bases and these probably prevent the transformation of the molecule into the *A* conformation.

The x-ray data alone does not directly give information about the sense of the double helix. Nevertheless, the fact that the deoxyribose sugar contains asymmetric carbon atoms, and that only one isomeric form occurs in DNA, means that a left-handed helical structure could not be the mirror image of a right-handed one. Left-handed and right-handed models can be built, both containing the same isomeric groups, and the model which is steriochemically more plausible should be the correct one. For the *A* conformation, only the right-handed model is steriochemically acceptable, whereas for the *B* conformation both types can be constructed, although the left-handed model is less satisfactory. Since it is possible to change from the *A* to the *B* conformation simply by varying the humidity, it is reasonable to assume that the DNA helix is also right-handed in the *B* conformation which exists *in vivo*.

c   The C conformation

The *C* form of DNA is produced by partial drying of Li DNA fibres. It only occurs at relative humidities less than 75%, and absence of lithium chloride in the fibres has the effect of making the DNA go into the semi-crystalline *C* form rather than the crystalline *B* form.

The conformation of the molecule in *C* DNA is similar to that in *B* DNA, except that it only contains $9\frac{1}{3}$ nucleotide pairs per turn of the helix of pitch 31 Å. Although the nucleotide conformation in *C* DNA is similar to that in *B* DNA, the base pairs are moved 2 Å away from the helix axis, and are tilted by about 5° (Marvin *et al.*, 1961).

d   Other conformations

When Na DNA fibres are kept under tension at 75% relative humidity it is possible to prevent the molecules from changing into the *A* conformation. Under these conditions the conformation of the molecule is similar to that in *B* DNA. When the fibres are stretched, the molecules are extended by more than half their length, and the bases tilt so that the internucleotide spacing along the molecule is increased to 5·4 Å.

e   The structure of DNA in vivo

X-ray diffraction photographs of intact sperm heads show that DNA exists in the *B* conformation *in vivo* (see Chapter 5).

Further evidence about the *in vivo* structure is obtained from diffraction photographs of bacterial DNA which has the ability to transfer streptomycin resistance to other bacteria. This transforming principle can be precipitated as fibres in 70% ethanol and stored without loss of activity. The state of hydration in the 70% ethanol is the same as in fibres of DNA at 92% relative humidity, and the x-ray diffraction patterns from transforming principle in 70% ethanol show that the molecules are in the *B* conformation.

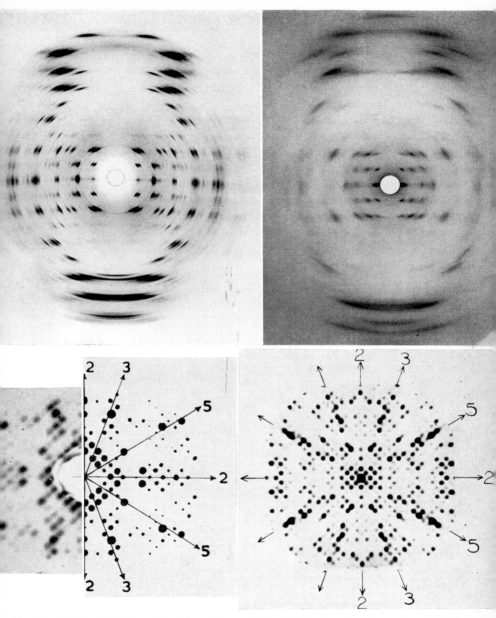

Plate 5. (a) *top left:* X-ray diffraction pattern of Na DNA in the *A* conformation at 75%
relative humidity. (b) *top right:* X-ray diffraction photograph of Na RNA from reovirus,
at 92% relative humidity (Langridge and Gomatos, 1964). (c) *bottom left:* X-ray diffraction pattern from a single crystal of tomato bushy stunt virus. The left half is a reproduction
of the actual diffraction pattern, and the right half is a diagram in which the spot size represents
the spot intensity in the diffraction pattern. The spikes of high intensity occur along directions
which are related as the five-, three- and two-fold axes of an icosahedron, and are indicated
by the arrows (courtesy of Dr. D. L. D. Caspar). (d) *bottom right:* An optical diffraction
pattern of 60 points arranged with icosahedral symmetry on the surface of a sphere. The
intensity distribution is similar to that in (c) (Caspar and Klug, 1962).

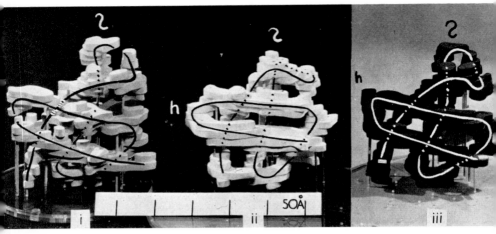

Plate 6. (a) Models of (i) sperm whale myoglobin, (ii) horse haemoglobin α-chain, (iii) horse haemoglobin β-chain, illustrating the similarity in the tertiary structure of the three chains (Perutz *et al.*, 1960).

Plate 6. (b) Model of haemoglobin molecule at 5·5 Å resolution, showing the two α-chains (white) and two β-chains (black) tetrahedrally arranged relative to each other (Perutz *et al.*, 1960).

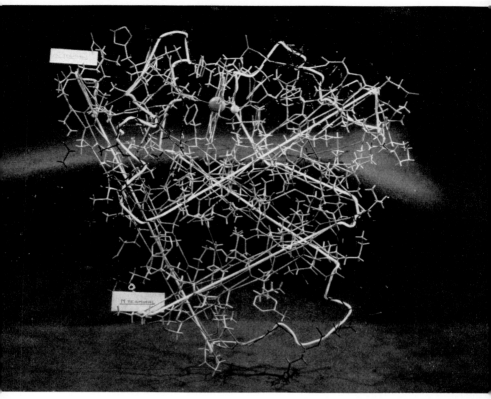

Plate 7. (a) Model showing the atomic arrangement in myoglobin as derived from the 2 Å Fourier synthesis. The haem group is viewed almost edge on, and the white cord shows the path of the polypeptide chain (Kendrew *et al.*, 1961).

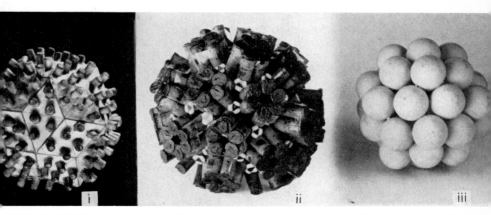

Plate 7. (b) Models representing the arrangement of subunits in the icosahedral protein shell with $T = 3$ (Caspar and Klug, 1962). (i) Each subunit is represented by a wooden peg. There are 3 subunits per equilateral face of the deltahedron, giving a total of 180 subunits. (ii) Each subunit is now represented by a piece of rubber tubing, and they cluster together at their outer ends to form 20 hexamers and 12 pentamers, which thus gives 32 morphological units. (iii) Each cluster is now represented by a ping-pong ball and this model with 32 ping-pong balls represents the appearance of the outer surface of (ii) at lower magnification. This model resembles the electron micrographs of turnip yellow mosaic virus.

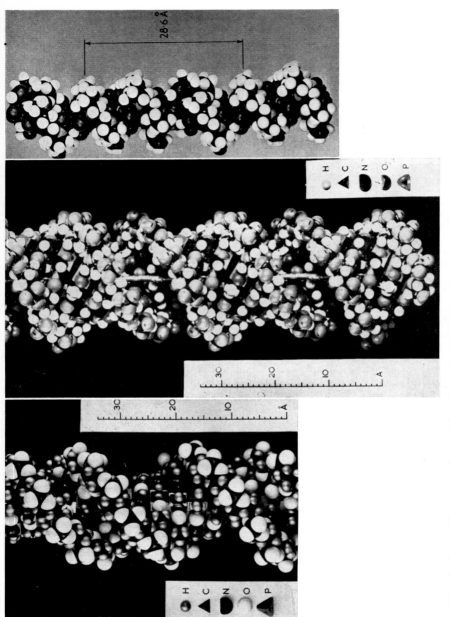

Plate 8. Space filling molecular models of (a) *left*: DNA in the *A* conformation. (b) *centre*: DNA in the *B* conformation. (c) *right*: Collagen (Rich and Crick, 1961).

f   The structure of DNA in solution

The amount of water in DNA fibres can reach a maximum of about 50% of the total weight before there is loss of orientation of the molecules. When the amount of water is increased beyond this value, a liquid-crystalline phase is produced which exists down to a DNA concentration of about 20%. When the DNA concentration is decreased further, a second phase is produced which is optically isotropic. Luzzati and his co-workers (Luzzati *et al.*, 1961, 1962) have made a detailed study of the low angle x-ray diffraction from these phases, and have shown that the mass per unit length of the molecules is in agreement with the Watson-Crick model for DNA.

4   Ribose Nucleic Acid (RNA)

The structure of RNA resisted solution for some time after the DNA structure had been established. The main obstacle was the poor quality of the x-ray diffraction photographs given by RNA fibres. They were too diffuse to be interpreted unambiguously, although in some respects they resembled those from DNA.

The chemical differences between RNA and DNA are small. The ribose sugar has an extra hydroxyl group attached to the C_2' atom and the uracil base lacks the CH_3 group which is attached to C_5 in thymine, but all the other components are the same. Thus it might be expected that the structure of RNA would be similar to that of DNA. However, the base analysis of RNA preparations did not show the equality of adenine to uracil and guanine to cytosine. With the discovery of the different types of RNA, namely messenger, ribosomal and transfer, it was obvious that the structure of these had to be considered separately.

Rich and Watson (1954a,b) made an x-ray study of RNAs from a variety of sources and showed that the diffraction patterns were essentially identical. These showed a fibre axis repeat of 28 Å and there were strong meridional or near meridional reflections corresponding to spacings of 3·3 Å and 4·0 Å. It could not be established with certainty, however, that the molecules were helical nor how many chains there were in a molecule.

A study of synthetic polyribonucleotides was undertaken by Rich and his co-workers in the hope that they would assist in the determination of the RNA structure. They showed (Rich and Davies,

8

1956) that the x-ray diffraction patterns from the synthetic poly-adenylic acid + polyuridylic acid were similar to those from DNA, which proved that it was possible for the polyribonucleotide chains to have a DNA-like conformation.

However, it was not until the study of crystalline preparations of RNA from yeast cells by Spencer, Fuller, Wilkins and Brown (1962) that the interpretation of the RNA x-ray diffraction patterns became possible. This was followed by studies of crystalline viral RNAs by Langridge and Gomatos (1963), Tomita and Rich (1964), and Langridge *et al.* (1964).

Crystallization was induced in the yeast RNA preparations by allowing a concentrated solution to dry slowly at 0°C, and pulling fibres from the gel before it had completely solidified. It was thought at the time that the crystallizable RNA was transfer RNA, but recent work suggests that it was probably fragments of ribosomal RNA (Spencer and Poole, 1965).

The diffraction pattern from these fibres showed that the RNA contained double-helical regions and that the conformation had similarities to the *A* conformation of DNA, with the bases tilted about 20° from perpendicular to the helix axis. The conformation remained almost unchanged over the relative humidity range 32–92%.

The diffraction pattern from crystalline yeast RNA clarified the nature of the diffuse patterns given by other RNA preparations. The sharp and diffuse patterns are essentially the same and all the diffuse regions on one can be related to the sharp regions of the other. This suggests that the helical regions in double-stranded viral RNA, ribosomal RNA and transfer RNA all have the same basic conformation.

Transfer RNA has a low molecular weight of just over 20,000, and it is known that each molecule consists of a single polynucleotide chain. Thus, in order to form double-helical regions, the molecule must fold back on itself. Model building shows that this is possible if at least three nucleotides are unpaired at the bends. The determination of the nucleotide sequence along alanine-transfer RNA by Holley *et al.* (1965) shows that only about one-third of the bases can form Watson-Crick type pairs, so that details of the conformation of the whole molecule have yet to be determined.

Langridge and Gomatos (1963) obtained high quality x-ray diffraction patterns from reovirus RNA, where chemical studies had shown that the molar ratio of adenine to uracil and of guanine to cytosine was close to unity (Gomatos and Tamm, 1963). The patterns were similar to those from crystalline yeast RNA but showed sharper reflections on the higher layer lines. From a careful study of the higher layer lines, Langridge and Gomatos showed that there are 10 nucleotide pairs per turn of the helix in RNA.

Similar conclusions were obtained by Tomita and Rich (1964) from a study of wound tumour virus RNA.

Although an RNA molecule may exist as a single chain in some viruses, a double-chain replicative form can exist within a cell during the process of producing new virus particles. X-ray diffraction studies of the replicative form of a bacteriophage RNA by Langridge *et al.* (1964) show that it has a similar conformation to that of yeast RNA and the double-stranded viral RNAs.

The analysis of RNA structure has not yet been carried to the stage where a detailed comparison with the DNA structure can be made. When this has been done, it should be possible to explain the differences between the polynucleotide chain conformations in DNA and RNA. It is probable that the hydroxyl group on the ribose sugar plays an important part in determining these differences.

a Constancy and change in RNA conformation

RNA extracted from tobacco mosaic virus (TMV) gives an x-ray pattern similar to that from other non-crystalline RNA preparations. This suggests that there are double helical regions in the molecule. However, the TMV RNA molecule is known to be a single polynucleotide chain, and in the TMV particle it exists as a single chain embedded in a helical array of subunits. This means that the extracted RNA molecule folds back on itself to form double helical regions.

Extracted ribosomal RNA gives the characteristic double-helical diffraction pattern, and an x-ray study of intact ribosomes (Zubay and Wilkins, 1960; Klug, Holmes and Finch, 1961) shows that the RNA within the ribosomes is in the same conformation.

5 Synthetic Polynucleotides

Since the discovery of the enzyme system that produces synthetic polyribonucleotides, extensive x-ray diffraction studies of these polymers have been made by Rich and his co-workers (Rich and Davies, 1956; Rich, 1957 and 1958; Rich *et al.*, 1961; Langridge and

Rich, 1963). These studies have shown that polyribonucleotide chains can form a variety of helical structures in which two, and sometimes three chains are hydrogen bonded together. Similar studies have also been made on synthetic deoxyribonucleotide polymers (Davies and Baldwin, 1963).

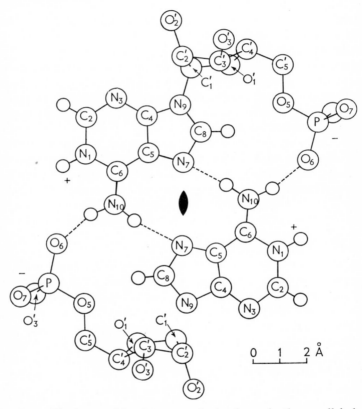

Fig. 4.11   The base-pairing between adenine bases in the parallel-chain double-stranded structure of polyadenylic acid. (From Rich *et al.*, 1961.)

Polyadenylic acid has been studied in more detail than any of the others (Rich *et al.*, 1961). At normal pH polyadenylic acid is a flexible random coil, but at acid pH it forms a rigid two-stranded molecule. The structure proposed for this is a double helix of parallel polynucleotide chains with eight nucleotide pairs per turn of the helix. The pitch of the helix is 30·4 Å and the bases are tilted about 10° from perpendicular to the helix axis.

A parallel arrangement of polynucleotide chains is also found in polycytidylic acid (Langridge and Rich, 1962). It is proposed that there are twelve nucleotide pairs per turn of a helix of pitch 37·3 Å.

Complexes which form between polyadenylic and polyuridylic acids, and between polyinosinic and polycytidylic acids give similar x-ray diffraction patterns to those of DNA and RNA. The two stranded polyadenylic-polyuricylic acid complex can further combine with another strand of polyuridylic acid to form a three-stranded helical structure (Felsenfeld, Davies and Rich, 1957).

A three-stranded structure is also formed by polyinosinic acid molecules, where the purine base is similar to guanine, but does not have an amino group attached to the six membered ring.

The study of these synthetic polynucleotides yields valuable information about the interaction between polynucleotide chains, a complete knowledge of which is necessary in order to explain some of the basic processes in the functioning of the living cell.

5 Nucleoproteins and Viruses

1 Introduction

Nucleic acids and proteins are often closely associated in living cells. In sperm heads and in chromosomes, DNA and protein are linked together; in ribosomes, RNA and protein occur together; and in viruses, either DNA or RNA is again associated with protein. In sperm heads and in viruses, the nucleic acid is in a stored or inactive state, but in chromosomes, and possibly in ribosomes, it is in an active state, so that knowledge of the way in which nucleic acid and protein interact in these structures may elucidate some of the steps in the processes of protein synthesis and cell regulation. Similarly, knowledge of the structure of viruses may clarify some of the basic principles involved in biological organisation.

2 Nucleoprotamines

Protamine is the protein found in conjunction with DNA mainly in the sperm of certain fish, e.g. trout and herring. About two-thirds of the amino acids in protamine are the basic residue arginine. The other amino acids are non-basic, and chemical analysis (Felix, 1953; Monier, 1956) shows that these occur in pairs along the polypeptide chain.

X-ray diffraction studies have been made on intact sperm heads, on extracted nucleoprotamine, and on complexes of DNA and protamine. They all give essentially identical diffraction patterns which are similar in many respects to those from *B* DNA. The similarity between the diffraction pattern from intact sperm heads and that from DNA fibres provides strong evidence that the structure of DNA in fibres is the same as that of DNA *in vivo* (Wilkins and Randall, 1953). Most of the x-ray diffraction studies have been made on dried material which is kept in a high humidity atmosphere during the x-ray exposure, a procedure which does not affect the *in vivo* structure because the same diffraction pattern is obtained from undried sperm which are alive at the beginning of the exposure.

Intact herring and trout sperm give the characteristic nucleoprotamine diffraction pattern, although oriented specimens cannot be prepared from these sperm. Oriented specimens can be prepared from *Sepia* (cuttle fish) and *Loligo* (squid) sperm because the sperm heads are elongated and they pack together parallel to each other in the spermatophore or in a fibre (Wilkins and Battaglia, 1953).

In nucleoprotamine the molecules are packed together in a hexagonal arrangement. The differences in intensity between the nucleoprotamine diffraction pattern and that from *B* DNA can be accounted for by considering the protamine as filling the shallower of the two grooves in the *B* DNA molecule (Feughelman *et al.*, 1955). Model building shows that a fully extended polyarginine chain, wound helically round the shallow groove, is such that the basic groups of the arginine can be in contact with the phosphate groups on DNA. Moreover, in order that all the basic groups should be neutralized by the phosphate groups, it is necessary to have at least two non-basic residues next to each other so that the chain can fold back into the correct position, exactly as the chemical studies show to be the case.

3 Nucleohistones

Nucleohistone is the main component of chromosomes. Histones have a larger molecular weight than protamines and also have a more complex amino acid composition, of which about 20% are basic residues. All the histone molecules in a given cell are not of the same composition and it is possible to separate them into various fractions depending on their amino acid composition.

Extracted nucleohistone can be pulled into fibres but the diffraction patterns they give are more diffuse than those from nucleoprotamine (see Plate IV). This makes accurate intensity measurements impossible and hence the conclusions about the structure more tentative. The meridional reflection corresponding to a periodicity of 3·4 Å, together with the 1st, 2nd and 3rd layer lines on the diffraction patterns are recognizably similar to those on the DNA *B*-type pattern, and show that the DNA conformation in nucleohistone is similar to that in DNA fibres. The difficulty lies in determining how the histone is arranged in the structure (Wilkins, Zubay and Wilson, 1959).

Polarized infra-red radiation studies of nucleohistone (Bradbury *et al.*, 1962) show that about half of the histone is in an α-helical conformation, and x-ray studies of isolated histone also show that

Nucleopoly-l-arginine

○ H

● Phosphate O

◉ O

◍ N

○ C

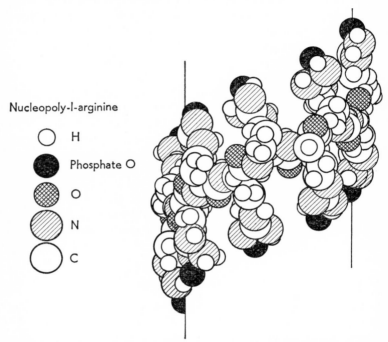

Fig. 5.1   (a) A model of poly-L-arginine wrapped around the shallow groove of DNA. (From Feughelman *et al.*, 1955.)

part of the histone conformation is α-helical. A near meridional reflection on the nucleohistone diffraction pattern, corresponding to a periodicity of 36 Å, could be due to α-helical histone bridges between parallel DNA molecules, with the α-helices fitting into the deeper grooves of the DNA molecules.

Powder diffraction patterns from intact calf thymus nuclei, chicken erythrocyte nuclei, and sea urchin sperm heads are similar to those from extracted nucleohistone, suggesting that the conclusions drawn from the fibre diffraction patterns are applicable to the structure *in vivo*.

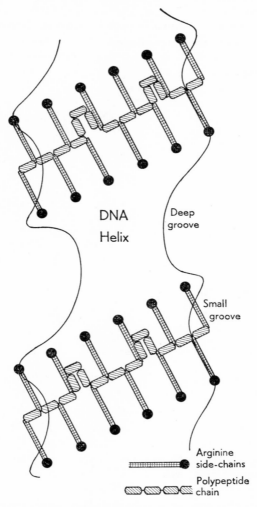

Fig. 5.1 (b) A diagrammatic representation of the proposed nucleo-protamine structure. The phosphate groups of DNA coincide with the black circles which represent the basic ends of the arginine side-groups. Non-basic residues are shown in pairs at folds in the polypeptide chain. (From Wilkins, 1955.)

Low angle x-ray diffraction studies of nucleohistone gels, of varying concentrations (Luzzati and Nicolaieff, 1963), show that a number of different phases can exist in solution. Different phases correspond to different states of aggregation of molecules.

DNA double helices

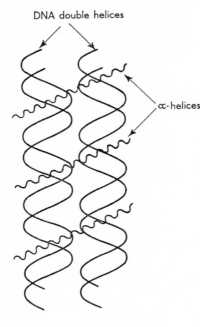

α-helices

Fig. 5.2 Diagrammatic representation of part of nucleohistone structure.

We can thus state that in both nucleoprotamine and nucleohistone, the DNA molecule is in the *B* conformation. In nucleoprotamine, the protamine is probably in the form of an extended polypeptide chain wrapped round the shallow groove of the DNA, while in nucleohistone part of the histone is in the α-helix conformation and may form bridges between adjacent DNA molecules by fitting into the deeper groove of DNA. The rather tentative nature of these conclusions in the case of nucleohistone indicates the necessity of further studies.

4   Ribosomes

Ribosomes are the sites of protein synthesis in living cells. Most of the information about their structure has so far come from ultracentrifuge and electron microscope studies. Ribosomes have not yet been crystallized, so that x-ray diffraction studies have only given a limited amount of structural information.

Most of the x-ray diffraction work has been done on ribosomes from *Escherichia coli* (*E. coli*), which exist in different states in solution, depending on the magnesium ion concentration. The different states are characterized by their sedimentation coefficients, 30S (Svedbergs), 50S, 70S and 100S, corresponding to molecular weights of 0·7, 1·8, 2·6 and 5·2 × 10^6 respectively. The composition of the different forms is the same; 64% RNA and 36% protein.

A 30S ribosome unit can combine with a 50S unit to form a 70S component, and two 70S units can link together through the 30S units to form a 100S ribosome which is about 380 Å long and about 150 Å wide. With increasing magnesium ion concentration, we can write 30S + 50S → 70S, and then 2(70S) → 100S, to represent the relationship between the various units.

X-ray diffraction patterns from 50S, 70S and 100S particles are essentially identical and show that the RNA conformation in wet ribosomes is the same as in extracted preparations (Zubay and Wilkins, 1960). Similar diffraction patterns are also obtained from rat liver and yeast ribosomes (Klug, Holmes and Finch, 1961).

Low angle x-ray diffraction studies of concentrated gels of 50S *E. coli* ribosomes (Langridge and Holmes, 1962) show that these particles can form a linear aggregate under such conditions.

5   Viruses

Viruses vary in the complexity of their structural organisation and composition, but the simplest kinds consist only of nucleic acid and protein. The protein acts as a protective covering for the nucleic acid, which is the infective part of the virus. A virus particle is inactive until it enters a living cell, when the nucleic acid is released

Table 5   Nucleic acid content of some simple viruses

Virus	% RNA
Tobacco mosaic	5
Tomato bushy stunt	17
Turnip yellow mosaic	37
Southern bean mosaic	21
Poliomyelitis	30

from its protein covering and initiates a process which produces new virus particles.

The simple viruses, which are the ones we are going to discuss, can be classified structurally into two main groups, rod-shaped viruses and spherical viruses. Both kinds have been shown to be constructed from protein subunits and x-ray diffraction studies have given information about the packing arrangements of the subunits in the virus particles. These studies have also, in some cases, given information about the location and the arrangement of the nucleic acid in the virus.

6   Tobacco Mosaic Virus

The virus which has been studied in greater detail than any other is the rod-shaped tobacco mosaic virus (TMV). It is composed of 95% protein and 5% RNA.

X-ray diffraction studies of TMV by Bernal and Fankuchen (1937 and 1941) showed that the virus particles were built up of a regular arrangement of subunits, although the actual arrangement was not determined. The specimens used in these studies were in the form of oriented gels, and were prepared by drawing the gel into a capillary tube and moving it up and down until it showed extinction between crossed polaroids. The capillary tube was then sealed and the specimen used to give fibre-type x-ray diffraction patterns.

Although TMV forms true crystals in infected plants, no crystals suitable for x-ray diffraction studies have so far been prepared from extracted material, and all the x-ray studies have been made on oriented gels as used by Bernal and Fankuchen. The concentration of TMV in the gels is about 20–30%, and the virus particles, which have a length of about 3000 Å and mean diameter of about 150 Å, lie with their long axes parallel to the axis of the tube. The virus particles are in random orientation about their axes, and, moreover, are not regularly arranged on a lattice. This means that the diffraction pattern is the cylindrically averaged diffraction from a single virus particle and the 'spots' on the diffraction pattern are maxima of the continuous transform rather than Bragg reflections. Interparticle interference effects are only appreciable in the central region along the equator, at smaller angles than those corresponding to a spacing of about 100 Å.

Watson (1954) showed that the TMV x-ray diffraction pattern was characteristic of that from a helical structure, and could be analyzed on the basis of a helical arrangement of protein subunits. The layer line spacing on the diffraction pattern is 69 Å and the intensity distribution is that expected from a helix with a pitch of 23 Å and with an integral number of subunits, $3n + 1$, in three turns of the helix. It follows that there should be a true meridional reflection on the $(3n + 1)$th layer line, but the difficulty of distinguishing between a near meridional and a true meridional reflection made it impossible to determine n in this way.

a   Number of subunits per turn

The number of subunits per turn of the helix was determined by Franklin and Holmes (1958) by comparing the equatorial diffraction from TMV with that from a mercury substituted TMV. Each protein subunit contains a single cysteine residue to which a mercury atom can be attached (Fraenkel-Conrat, 1959).

The intensity distribution along the equator depends on the distribution of scattering matter in a projection of the structure down the specimen axis. When the Hg-TMV particle is viewed in projection down its axis there should be $3n + 1$ mercury atoms arranged along the circumference of a circle. The mercury atoms should affect the equatorial diffraction in two ways, one depending on the actual radius at which they are situated, r_{Hg}, and the other depending on their separation along the circumference. This latter effect is confined to the outer regions of the equator.

From an analysis of the inner region of the equator, r_{Hg} was found to be 56·2 Å, and from an inspection of the outer region, $3n + 1$ was found to be 49.

Prior to this, Franklin and Klug (1955) had observed that some of the layer lines on the TMV diffraction pattern were split, showing that the number of subunits per turn was not exactly $3n + 1$. From the amount of splitting they found that in the common strain of TMV the number of subunits in the 69 Å repeat distance was $(3n + 1·02) \pm 0·01$.

b   Dimensions of the TMV particle

The length of TMV particles, as determined by electron microscope studies, is about 3000 Å. This value is probably shorter than the length *in vivo* because of the dehydration which takes place in

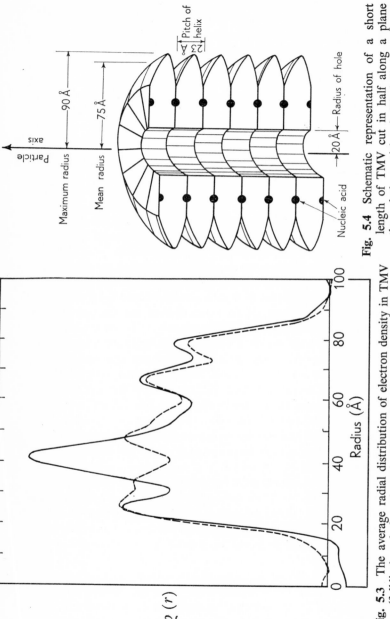

Fig. 5.3 The average radial distribution of electron density in TMV (full line), and of repolymerized RNA-free virus protein (broken line) as determined from the equatorial x-ray scattering. The central hole is seen to have a radius of about 20 Å, the maximum external radius is about 90 Å, and the RNA is at a radius of 40 Å. (From Franklin

Fig. 5.4 Schematic representation of a short length of TMV cut in half along a plane through the particle axis. The helical groove on the outside of the particle can be seen, together with the hole down the centre of the particle. The RNA is shown at a radius of 40 Å. (From

preparing the specimen for the electron microscope. This is suggested by the work of Markham *et al.* (1964), who applied an elegant electron microscope technique to show that the TMV helix is left-handed and with a pitch of 17·85 Å. This value is smaller than the 23 Å derived from the x-ray diffraction results, and if it is due to shrinkage on dehydration then the *in vivo* length of TMV is about 3800 Å.

The interparticle distance derived from x-ray studies of dry TMV specimens is 152 Å, which is in agreement with electron microscope measurements. However, the diameter of isolated particles appeared to be greater than this. From an analysis of the intensity distribution along the third layer line of the TMV diffraction pattern Franklin and Klug (1956) showed that the outside of the TMV particle is grooved, so that the mean radius of the particle is 77 Å, but the maximum radius is about 90 Å. The helically grooved particles can interlock when they come close together in the dry state, so that the interparticle distance is less than the maximum particle diameter.

By comparing the equatorial diffraction from TMV and lead substituted TMV, Caspar (1956a) determined the phases of the diffraction maxima, knowledge of which enabled him to calculate the average radial distribution of scattering matter in TMV. Caspar's analysis showed that the maximum radius of TMV was about 90 Å.

c Radial distribution of matter in TMV

Caspar's determination of the average radial distribution of scattering matter in TMV also showed that the virus particle had a central hole of diameter 35–40 Å. This was confirmed by Franklin (1956), using mercury-substituted TMV. The central hole was subsequently directly observed in electron micrographs (Huxley, 1957).

d Location of RNA in TMV

TMV can be dissociated into protein subunits and RNA, and the protein subunits can be reaggregated to produce a rod-like structure similar to the intact virus. Comparison of the average radial distribution of scattering matter in the repolymerized protein rod with that in TMV by Franklin (1956) showed that the RNA in TMV was located at a radial distance of about 40 Å.

Since the length of the TMV particle is known, and also the number of subunits in a length of 69 Å, the total number of subunits can be calculated. Also, knowing the molecular weight of the RNA, the total number of nucleotides can be calculated. This shows that three nucleotides are associated with each protein subunit. Differences between the TMV and RNA-free protein diffraction patterns can be explained as due to a single RNA chain which follows the protein subunit helix. There should, therefore, be 49 nucleotides in one turn of a helix of pitch 23 Å.

e   Protein subunit structure in TMV

The arrangement of the protein subunits represents the quaternary structure of TMV, and this is what the x-ray studies have so far

Fig. 5.5   A drawing of part of the structure of TMV as derived from x-ray diffraction studies. Part of the RNA chain is shown without the surrounding protein subunits. (From Klug and Caspar, 1960.)

determined. The primary structure of the polypeptide chain within a subunit is known from chemical sequence analysis, but the secondary and tertiary structures have not yet been determined, although there is evidence that part of the chain has an α-helical conformation.

The x-ray diffraction analysis suggests that the protein subunit has an ellipsoidal shape with one principal axis of about 70 Å and the other two about 20–25 Å.

7 Other Rod-Shaped Viruses

Little x-ray diffraction work has been done on rod-shaped viruses which are very different from TMV. Studies of other strains of TMV, however, show that the exact number of subunits in the repeat period of 69 Å varies from 49.05 in one strain to 48.98 in another. The packing arrangement of the subunits would be very similar in all these particles, and, apart from the subunits at the ends of the particles, each subunit would be equivalent and would form the same type of bonds with its neighbours.

In one strain of TMV, Caspar and Holmes (1962) have found an interesting difference which suggests that identical subunits pack together in a quasi-equivalent arrangement. This result has a bearing on the theories proposed by Caspar and Klug (1962) concerning the physical principles involved in the construction of virus particles which are discussed later.

8 Spherical Viruses

In contrast to the TMV studies, which have been made on oriented gels, those of spherical viruses have been made on crystalline specimens. The first spherical virus to be crystallized was tomato bushy stunt virus (BSV), by Bawden and Pirie (1938), and the first x-ray diffraction studies were made by Bernal, Fankuchen and Riley (1938). Bernal *et al.* used powder specimens consisting of a random arrangement of small crystals. Single crystal photographs were first obtained by Crowfoot and Schmidt (1945), from tobacco necrosis virus, and single crystal photographs of BSV were obtained by Carlisle and Dornberger (1948). These studies showed that the unit cell shape in BSV was cubic with $a = 386$ Å, but they did not reveal the symmetry of the lattice.

The first systematic analysis that revealed the lattice symmetry and also the symmetry of the virus particle was made on BSV by Caspar (1956b). This was soon followed by the analysis of turnip yellow mosaic virus (TYMV) by Klug, Finch and Franklin (1957a,b) and later by the analysis of polio virus (Finch and Klug, 1959), and of Southern bean mosaic virus (SBMV) (Magdoff, 1960).

a   X-ray diffraction studies of virus solutions

The low angle scattering of x-rays from dilute solutions of virus particles gives information about the average size of the particles

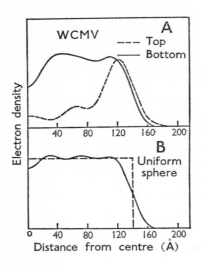

Fig. 5.6 (A) The average radial distribution of electron density inside wild cucumber mosaic virus (full line) and the RNA-free 'top component' (broken line) as calculated from the Fourier transform of the scattered amplitudes.
(B) The Fourier transform (full line) of the theoretical scattering amplitudes from a uniform sphere of 140 Å radius, which, for comparison with (A) was calculated for the same angular range. (From Anderegg *et al.*, 1961.)

and about the average electron density distribution within the particle. Low angle studies have been made on BSV and SBMV (Leonard *et al.*, 1953), TYMV (Schmidt *et al.*, 1954), wild cucumber virus (Anderegg and Geil, 1959), and polio virus (Finch, 1959). The average diameter of BSV particles was found to be 309 Å, and all the others have values close to 280 Å. The spherically averaged radial electron density in the particles is approximately uniform.

A similar analysis of RNA-free TYMV (Schmidt *et al.*, 1954) and RNA-free cucumber mosaic virus (Anderegg and Geil, 1959; Anderegg *et al.*, 1961) shows that these particles are in the form of hollow spherical shells, which indicates that most of the RNA is centrally located inside a protein shell in the intact virus.

b   X-ray diffraction by single crystals

The fact that virus particles form single crystals proves that all the particles are of the same size, and in this respect they resemble molecules. Virus crystals, like protein crystals, contain a large amount of water which is necessary for the perfection of the crystal. When the water is allowed to evaporate the particles become disordered in the crystal and the quality of the x-ray diffraction pattern deteriorates, with loss of detail in the outer region. It is therefore necessary to mount the virus crystals in a thin-walled glass or quartz tube which also contains a small amount of the mother liquor. Some virus crystals are unstable at room temperature and have to be maintained at about 5°C during x-ray exposure.

The large size of the unit cell, and hence the large number of diffraction spectra, means that the collection of intensity data from a virus crystal is an immense problem. Added difficulties arise because the exposure time has to be long and also because the crystals are sensitive to x-ray irradiation. However, it is possible to draw conclusions about the symmetry of virus particles merely from an inspection of the general distribution of the diffracted x-ray intensity.

c   Symmetry of spherical viruses

Crick and Watson (1956) suggested that simple viruses are either rod-shaped or spherical because they are built up of subunits which are packed together in a regular manner. It was known that TMV was constructed from subunits which were in a helical arrangement. This meant that all the subunits were equivalent and could form similar type bonds with neighbouring subunits.

A helical arrangement, therefore, represents the general way in which a rod-like structure can be built from identical subunits. The symmetry operation which produces equivalence is the screw of the helix.

In the case of a spherical virus, the problem that Crick and Watson considered was that of producing an equivalent arrangement of subunits around a point; in other words, of arranging units on the surface of a sphere so that each unit was in the same environment. Since proteins contain only L-type amino acids, the only allowed symmetry operation is that of rotation. An arrangement of rotation axes through a point constitutes a point group and the most probable ones that apply to spherical viruses are those of the cubic point groups. There are three cubic point groups that contain rotation axes only, and each has at least four three-fold rotation axes so related that they point along the four diagonals of a cube. They are referred to as 23 (two-three), 432 (four-three-two) and 532 (five-three-two) point groups, or, because these symmetries apply to Platonic solids, the groups are said to have tetrahedral, octahedral

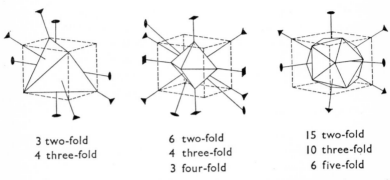

3 two-fold	6 two-fold	15 two-fold
4 three-fold	4 three-fold	10 three-fold
	3 four-fold	6 five-fold

Fig. 5.7 Diagrams showing (a) a tetrahedron, (b) an octahedron and (c) an icosahedron, inscribed in a cube. The number and type of rotation axes of the tetrahedron, octahedron and icosahedron are also listed, and some of these are shown in the diagrams.

and icosahedral symmetry respectively. The number of asymmetric units which are required by 23 symmetry is 12, by 432 symmetry is 24, and by 532 symmetry is 60.

The early x-ray diffraction studies of BSV and of TYMV had shown that these viruses crystallized in a cubic unit cell, but had not established that the symmetry was cubic. In a systematic analysis of BSV, Caspar (1956b) showed that the crystal symmetry was cubic, and, furthermore, that the virus particle had 532 (or icosahedral) symmetry. Space groups and lattices do not possess five-fold axes, but Caspar showed that the existence of such non-crystallographic symmetry axes could be detected by 'spikes' of high intensity, extending from the centre of the diffraction pattern along the direction of the symmetry axes (Plate V).

Similar conclusions were reached regarding the symmetry of TYMV (Klug *et al.*, 1957b), polio virus (Finch and Klug, 1959) and SBMV (Magdoff, 1960).

Evidence that the icosahedral symmetry applies only to the protein shell of the virus was provided by a comparison of the diffraction patterns from TYMV and from RNA-free TYMV (Klug and Finch, 1960). The spikes of strong intensity along the symmetry axes were more enhanced in the RNA-free TYMV pattern, suggesting that the protein shell had 532 symmetry but that the whole virus particle, including the nucleic acid, probably had only 32 symmetry.

The x-ray diffraction results, therefore, show that the protein shell of the virus particles possesses icosahedral symmetry, which means that the number of subunits forming the shell is 60 or a multiple of 60. If the subunits are identical *and* are equivalently arranged, then the number must be 60, but if they are identical but *not* equivalently arranged then the number can be a multiple of 60.

d Virus shell structure

The other physical technique used to study virus structure is that of electron microscopy. The shadow casting method showed that some viruses had the shape of a regular icosahedron (Williams and Smith, 1958), but it was the high resolution studies of adenovirus by Horne *et al.* (1959) that first revealed the detailed surface structure of a virus particle. The term 'morphological unit' is used to describe the surface features which are revealed in the electron micrographs. Adenovirus had 252 morphological units on its surface.

Similar studies of TYMV revealed 32 morphological units (Huxley and Zubay, 1960; Nixon and Gibbs, 1960), which meant that the morphological units could not be identified with the crystallographic subunits. In studies of other viruses, 12, 42, 162 and 812 morphological units were reported, but in no case was it 60 or a multiple of 60.

In an elegant theory, based on a consideration of the physical principles involved in the construction of virus shells, Caspar and Klug (1962) have shown how the morphological and crystallographic subunits can be related.

Prior to Caspar and Klug's theory, Horne and Wildy (1961) had suggested that the morphological units were of two kinds, one having six-fold and the other having five-fold symmetry. By considering a hexagon associated with the six-fold unit and a pentagon with the five-fold unit, they examined the geometrical problem of forming closed surfaces built from hexagons and pentagons arranged with icosahedral symmetry. This geometrical approach, while showing that the total number of hexagons and pentagons was equal to the number of morphological units, did not consider the underlying physical principles in protein shell formation.

Caspar and Klug's theory gives a physical explanation of how the protein shell is constructed and, moreover, suggests how the virus shell could be built by a process of self-assembly of subunits. Their

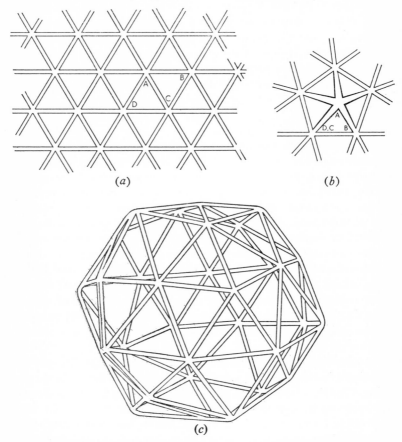

(a)

(b)

(c)

Fig. 5.8 The folding of a six-fold net to form a closed surface. (a) a plane six-fold net, (b) a 5-vertex formed from a 6-vertex by cutting the lattice along a line joining adjacent lattice points, e.g., AC in (a), and folding the net so that adjacent equilateral triangles are super- imposed. This produces a curvature of the net. (c) a closed surface with 60 equilateral triangular facets (T = 3 in Caspar and Klug's designation).

theory was inspired by the principles of efficient design applied by Buckminster Fuller in the construction of geodesic domes.

The basic assumptions of Caspar and Klug's theory are as follows: firstly, all the subunits (or structure units) are identical, and, secondly, the subunits are arranged so that they are quasi-equivalently related. Thus, they drop the concept of strict mathematical equivalence, which would limit the number of subunits to 60, but retain its physical essentials, because quasi-equivalence means that the same type of bonds are formed between all the subunits, although these bonds may be deformed slightly in different environments on the surface. In the case of one strain of TMV, Caspar and Holmes (1962) have shown that there is quasi-equivalence of the helically arranged subunits, so it is reasonable to assume that the same may be the case with spherical viruses.

The problem of quasi-equivalence in the case of spherical viruses can be considered from the point of view of folding a plane net to form a closed surface. This can only be done with a square net, with four-fold symmetry; or a triangular net, with six-fold symmetry. By folding a square net, a corner is formed where three edges of the net meet, compared to four edges when it was planar. Similarly, with the triangular net, vertices can be formed where 5, 4 or 3 edges meet, compared to six when it is planar. If either twelve 5-vertices, six 4-vertices or four 3-vertices are formed, then a closed surface is produced with faces which are equilateral triangles. When real subunits are associated with the plane net, departure from equivalence is least when a 5-vertex is formed because the deformation of the bonds between subunits is then least.

Polyhedra formed by folding a triangular net have equilateral triangular faces and are called deltahedra. The icosahedron has 20 equilateral triangular faces, and Caspar and Klug have shown that all deltahedra which possess icosahedral symmetry have $20T$ facets where T is a triangulation number given by $T = Pf^2$, with P having any of the values 1, 3, 7, 13, 19, 21, 31, ... ($= h^2 + hk + k^2$, for all pairs of integers h and k which have no common factor), and f is any integer. The structure unit of the virus shell can be considered as one-third of a triangular facet, so that the total number of quasi-equivalent units in the shell is $60T$. If these structure units cluster together in groups of six (hexamers) and in groups of five (pentamers), at the 6- and 5-vertices respectively, then there will be 12 pentamers and $10(T - 1)$ hexamers. These clusters would correspond to the morphological units seen in the electron microscope, so that there should be $12 + 10(T - 1) = 10T + 2$ of them. For TYMV, for example, with 32 morphological units, $T = 3$, and the total number of structure units should therefore be 180. Since $T = 3$ for TYMV, $P = 3$ and $f = 1$. Viruses with 12, 42, 92 and 162 morphological units fall into the $P = 1$ class, while those with 72 units are in the $P = 7$ class. All deltahedra in the $P \geqslant 7$ classes are skew and are of two kinds, which are mirror images of each other.

For the detailed structure analysis which is necessary to test Caspar and Klug's theory, and also to determine the secondary and tertiary structure of the polypeptide chain in the subunits, as well as the arrangement of the nucleic acid in the virus particle, the phases of the diffracted x-ray spectra must be determined. Such a detailed analysis presents one of the most formidable problems in x-ray crystallography.

References

ANDEREGG, J. W. and GEIL, P. H. (1959). In *Proceedings of the First National Biophysics Conference* (U.S.A.). Eds. H. QUASTLER and H. MOROWITZ. New Haven: Yale Univ. Press.

ANDEREGG, J. W., GEIL, P. H., BEEMAN, W. W. and KAESBERG, P. (1961). *Biophys. J.*, **1**, 657.

ARNDT, U. W. and PHILLIPS, D. C. (1961). *Acta Cryst.*, **14**, 807.

ARNOTT, S., WILKINS, M. H. F., HAMILTON, L. D. and LANGRIDGE, R. (1965). *J. Mol. Biol.*, **11**, 391.

ASTBURY, W. T. (1938). *Trans. Faraday Soc.*, **34**, 378.

ASTBURY, W. T. (1941). *Chem. Indust.*, **60**, 491.

ASTBURY, W. T. and BELL, F. O. (1938). *Cold Spring Harbor Symp. Quant. Biol.*, **6**, 109.

ASTBURY, W. T. and BELL, F. O. (1941). *Nature*, **147**, 696.

ASTBURY, W. T., DICKINSON, S. and BAILEY, K. (1935). *Biochem. J.*, **29**, 2351.

ASTBURY, W. T. and STREET, A. (1931). *Phil. Trans. A*, **230**, 75.

ASTBURY, W. T. and WOODS, H. J. (1933). *Phil. Trans. A*, **232**, 333.

BAMFORD, C. H., HANBY, W. E. and HAPPEY, F. (1951). *Proc. Roy. Soc. A*, **205**, 30.

BAMFORD, C. H., BROWN, L., ELLIOTT, A., HANBY, W. E. and TROTTER, I. F. (1953). *Proc. Roy. Soc. B*, **141**, 49.

BAMFORD, C. H., BROWN, L., ELLIOTT, A., HANBY, W. E. and TROTTER, I. F. (1954). *Nature*, **173**, 27.

BAWDEN, F. C. and PIRIE, N. W. (1938). *Nature*, **141**, 513.

BEAR, R. S. (1956). *J. Biophys. Biochem. Cytol.*, **2**, 363.

BERNAL, J. D. and CROWFOOT, D. (1934). *Nature*, **133**, 794.

BERNAL, J. D. and FANKUCHEN, I. (1937). *Nature*, **139**, 923.

BERNAL, J. D. and FANKUCHEN, I. (1941). *J. Gen. Physiol.*, **25**, 111.

BERNAL, J. D., FANKUCHEN, I. and PERUTZ, M. F. (1938). *Nature*, **141**, 523.

BERNAL, J. D., FANKUCHEN, I. and RILEY, D. P. (1938). *Nature*, **142**, 1075.

BLAKE, C. C. F., FENN, R. H., NORTH, A. C. T., PHILLIPS, D. C. and POLJAK, R. J., STANFORD, R. H., MARSH, R. E. and COREY, R. B.; DICKERSON, R. E., REDDY, J. M., PINKERTON, M. and STEINRAUF, (1962). *Nature*, **196**, 1173.

BLOW, D. M. and CRICK, F. H. C. (1959). *Acta Cryst.*, **12**, 794.

BLOW, D. M. and ROSSMANN, M. G. (1961). *Acta Cryst.*, **14**, 1195.

BODO, G., DINTZIS, H. M., KENDREW, J. C. and WYCKOFF, H. W. (1959). *Proc. Roy. Soc. A*, **253**, 70.

BRADBURY, E. M., BROWN, L., DOWNIE, A. R., ELLIOTT, A., FRASER, R. D. B., HANBY, W. E. and MCDONALD, T. R. R. (1960). *J. Mol. Biol.*, **2**, 276.

BRADBURY, E. M., PRICE, W. C., WILKINSON, G. R. and ZUBAY, G. (1962). *J. Mol. Biol.*, **4**, 50.

131

BRAGG, W. L. (1913). *Proc. Cambridge Phil. Soc.*, **17**, 43.

BRAGG, W. L. (1939). *Nature*, **143**, 678.

BRAGG, W. L., KENDREW, J. C. and PERUTZ, M. F. (1950). *Proc. Roy. Soc. A*, **203**, 321.

BRAGG, W. L. and PERUTZ, M. F. (1952a). *Acta Cryst.*, **5**, 277.

BRAGG, W. L. and PERUTZ, M. F. (1952b). *Acta Cryst.*, **5**, 323.

BRAGG, W. L. and PERUTZ, M. F. (1952c). *Proc. Roy. Soc. A*, **213**, 425.

BRAGG, W. L. and PERUTZ, M. F. (1954). *Proc. Roy. Soc. A*, **225**, 315.

BRILL, R. (1923). *Liebigs Ann.*, **434**, 204.

BROWN, D. M. and TODD, A. R. (1955). In *The Nucleic Acids*, Vol. 1, Eds. E. CHARGAFF and J. N. DAVIDSON. New York: Academic Press.

BROWN, L. and TROTTER, I. F. (1956). *Trans. Faraday Soc.*, **52**, 537.

BUERGER, M. J. (1959). *Vector Space*. New York: Wiley.

BURNS, D. M. and IBALL, J. (1960). *Proc. Roy. Soc.*, *A*, **257**, 491.

CARLISLE, C. H. and DORNBERGER, K. (1948). *Acta Cryst.*, **1**, 194.

CARPENTER, G. B. and DONOHUE, J. (1950). *J. Amer. Chem. Soc.*, **72**, 7899.

CASPAR, D. L. D. (1956a). *Nature*, **177**, 928.

CASPAR, D. L. D. (1956b). *Nature*, **177**, 475.

CASPAR, D. L. D. and HOLMES, K. C. (1962). See CASPAR, D. L. D. (1963). In *Adv. Protein Chem.*, **19**.

CASPAR, D. L. D. and KLUG, A. (1962). *Cold Spring Harbor Symp. Quant. Biol.*, **27**, 1.

CHARGAFF, E. (1950). *Experientia*, **6**, 201.

COCHRAN, W. and CRICK, F. H. C. (1952). *Nature*, **168**, 684.

COCHRAN, W., CRICK, F. H. C. and VAND, V. (1952). *Acta Cryst.*, **5**, 581.

COHEN, C. and BEAR, R. S. (1953). *J. Amer. Chem. Soc.*, **75**, 2783.

COHEN, C. and HOLMES, K. C. (1963). *J. Mol. Biol.*, **6**, 423.

COREY, R. B. (1938). *J. Amer. Chem. Soc.*, **60**, 1598.

COREY, R. B. and PAULING, L. (1955). *Rc. Ist. lomb. Sci. Lett.*, **89**, 10.

COWAN, P., NORTH, A. C. T. and RANDALL, J. T. (1953). *The Nature and Structure of Collagen*. Ed. J. T. RANDALL. London: Butterworth, p. 241.

COWAN, P. M. and MCGAVIN, S. (1955). *Nature*, **176**, 501.

COWAN, P. M., MCGAVIN, S. and NORTH, A. C. T. (1955). *Nature*, **176**, 1062.

CRICK, F. H. C. (1952). *Nature*, **170**, 882.

CRICK, F. H. C. (1953). *Acta Cryst.*, **6**, 685.

CRICK, F. H. C. and RICH, A. (1955). *Nature*, **176**, 780.

CRICK, F. H. C. and WATSON, J. D. (1956). *Nature*, **177**, 473.

CROWFOOT, D. (1935). *Nature*, **135**, 591.

CROWFOOT, D. and SCHMIDT, G. M. J. (1945). *Nature*, **155**, 504.

CULLIS, A. F., MUIRHEAD, H., PERUTZ, M. F., ROSSMANN, M. G. and NORTH, A. C. T. (1961). *Proc. Roy. Soc. A*, **265**, 15.

CULLIS, A. F., MUIRHEAD, H., PERUTZ, M. F., ROSSMANN, M. G. and NORTH, A. C. T. (1962). *Proc. Roy. Soc. A*, **265**, 161.

DAVIES, D. R. and BALDWIN, R. L. (1963). *J. Mol. Biol.*, **6**, 251.

EDMUNDSON, A. B. and HIRS, C. H. W. (1961). *Nature*, **190**, 663.

ELLIOT, A. and MALCOLM, B. R. (1956). *Nature*, **178**, 912.

ELLIOT, A. and MALCOLM, B. R. (1959). *Proc. Roy. Soc. A*, **249**, 30.

FELIX, K. (1953). In *The Chemical Structure of Protein*. London: J. & A. CHURCHILL.

FELSENFELD, G., DAVIES, D. R. and RICH, A. (1957). *J. Amer. Chem. Soc.*, **79**, 2023.

FEUGHELMAN, M., LANGRIDGE, R., SEEDS, W. E., STOKES, A. R., WILSON, H. R., HOOPER, C. W., WILKINS, M. H. F., BARCLAY, R. K. and HAMILTON, L. D. (1955). *Nature*, **175**, 834.

FINCH, J. T. (1959). Ph.D. Thesis, London University.

FINCH, J. T. and KLUG, A. (1959). *Nature*, **183**, 1709.

FRAENKEL-CONRAT, H. (1959). In *Symposium on Sulphur in Proteins*. Ed. R. BENESCH. New York: Academic Press.

FRANKLIN, R. E. (1956). *Nature*, **177**, 929.

FRANKLIN, R. E. and GOSLING, R. G. (1933a). *Nature*, **171**, 737.

FRANKLIN, R. E. and GOSLING, R. G. (1953b). *Nature*, **172**, 156.

FRANKLIN, R. E. and KLUG, A. (1955). *Acta Cryst.*, **8**, 777.

FRANKLIN, R. E., KLUG, A. and HOLMES, K. C. (1957). *Ciba Foundation Symposium on the Nature of Viruses*. London: J. & A. Churchill, p. 39.

FRANKLIN, R. E. and HOLMES, K. C. (1958). *Acta Cryst.*, **11**, 213.

FRASER, R. D. B. and MacRAE, T. P. (1962). *J. Mol. Biol.*, **5**, 457.

FRASER, R. D. B., MacRAE, T. P. and MILLER, A. (1964). *J. Mol. Biol.*, **10**, 147.

FRASER, R. D. B., MacRAE, T. P. and MILLER, A. (1964). *Acta Cryst.*, **17**, 813.

FRIEDRICH, W., KNIPPING, P. and LAUE, M. VON. (1912). *Sitzg. math. phys. Klasse bayer*. Akad. Wiss. Munchen, p. 303.

FULLER, W., WILKINS, M. H. F., WILSON, H. R. and HAMILTON, L. D. (1965). *J. Mol. Biol.* **12**, 60.

FURBERG, S. (1950). *Acta Cryst.*, **3**, 325.

GOMATOS, P. J. and TAMM, I. (1963). *Proc. Nat. Acad. Sci. U.S.A.*, **49**, 707.

GREEN, D. W., INGRAM, V. M. and PERUTZ, M. F. (1954). *Proc. Roy. Soc. A*, **225**, 287.

HANSON, J. and HUXLEY, H. (1955). *Symp. Soc. Exp. Biol.*, **9**, 228.

HARKER, D. (1956). *Acta Cryst.*, **9**, 1.

HASCHMEYER, A. E. V. and SOBELL, H. M. (1963). *Proc. Nat. Acad. Sci. U.S.A.*, **50**, 872.

HERZOG, R. O. and JANCKE, W. (1920). *Ber. dtsch. Chem. Ges.*, **53**, 2162.

HODGKIN, D. C. (1960). *Nature*, **188**, 441.

HODGKIN, D. C., KAMPER, J., LINDSAY, J., MACKAY, M. PICKWORTH, J., ROBERTSON, J. H., SCHOEMAKER, C. B., WHITE, J. G., PROSEN, R. J. and TRUEBLOOD, K. N. (1957). *Proc. Roy. Soc. A*, **242**, 228.

HOLLEY, R. W., APGAR, J., EVERETT, G. A., MADISON, J. T., MARQUISEE, M., MERRILL, S. H., PENSWICK, J. R. and ZAMIR, A. (1965). *Science*, **147**, 1462.

HOOGSTEEN, K. (1959). *Acta Cryst.*, **12**, 822.

HORNE, R. W., BRENNER, S., WATERSON, A. P. and WILDY, P. (1959). *J. Mol. Biol.*, **1**, 84.

HORNE, R. W. and WILDY, P. (1961). *Virology*, **15**, 348.

HUGGINS, M. L. (1943). *Chem. Rev.*, **32**, 195.

HUGHES, E. W. and MOORE, W. J. (1949). *J. Amer. Chem. Soc.*, **71**, 2618.

HUXLEY, H. E. (1951). *Discuss. Farad. Soc.*, No. 11, p. 148.

134   *Diffraction of X-rays*

HUXLEY, H. E. (1952). Ph.D. Thesis, Cambridge University.

HUXLEY, H. E. (1953). *Proc. Roy. Soc. B*, **141**, 59.

HUXLEY, H. E. (1957) *Proceedings of the Stockholm Conference on Electron Microscopy.* Eds. F. SJÖSTRAND and J. RHODIN. New York: Academic Press.

HUXLEY, H. E. and PERUTZ, M. F. (1951). *Nature*, **167**, 1057.

HUXLEY, H. E. and ZUBAY, G. (1960). *J. Mol. Biol.*, **2**, 189.

INGRAM, D. J. E. and KENDREW, J. C. (1956). *Nature*, **178**, 906.

KENDREW, J. C. (1963). *Science*, **139**, 1259.

KENDREW, J. C., BODO, G., DINTZIS, H. M., PARRISH, R. G., WYCKOFF, H. and PHILLIPS, D. C. (1958). *Nature*, **181**, 662.

KENDREW, J. C., DICKERSON, R. E., STRANDBERG, B. E., HART, R. G., DAVIES, D. R., PHILLIPS, D. C. and SHORE, V. C. (1960). *Nature*, **185**, 422.

KENDREW, J. C., WATSON, H. C., STRANDBERG, B. E., DICKERSON, R. E., PHILLIPS, D. C. and SHORE, V. C. (1961). *Nature*, **190**, 666.

KLUG, A., FINCH, J. T. and FRANKLIN, R. E. (1957a). *Nature*, **179**, 683.

KLUG, A., FINCH, J. T. and FRANKLIN, R. E. (1957b). *Biochim. Biophys. Acta*, **25**, 242.

KLUG, A. and CASPAR, D. L. D. (1960). *Advances in Virus Res.*, **7**, 225.

KLUG, A., HOLMES, K. C. and FINCH, J. T. (1961). *J. Mol. Biol.*, **3**, 87.

KOSTER, D., KNOL, K. S. and PRINS, J. A. (1930). *Z. Physik.*, **63**, 345.

KRAUT, J., SIEKER, L. C., HIGH, D. F. and FREER, S. T. (1962). *Proc. Nat. Acad. Sci. U.S.A.*, **48**, 1417.

KRAUT, J., HIGH, D. F. and SIEKER, L. C. (1964). *Proc. Nat. Acad. Sci. U.S.A.*, **51**, 839.

LANG, A. R. (1956). *Acta Cryst.*, **9**, 436.

LANGRIDGE, R., BILLETER, M. A., BORST, P., BURDOM, R. H. and WEISSMANN, C. (1964). *Proc. Nat. Acad. Sci. U.S.A.*, **52**, 114.

LANGRIDGE, R. and HOLMES, K. C. (1962). *J. Mol. Biol.*, **5**, 611.

LANGRIDGE, R. and GOMATOS, P. J. (1963). *Science*, **141**, 694.

LANGRIDGE, R. and RICH, A. (1960). *Acta Cryst.*, **13**, A 1052.

LANGRIDGE, R. and RICH, A. (1963). *Nature*, **198**, 725.

LANGRIDGE, R., WILSON, H. R., HOOPER, C. W., WILKINS, M. H. F. and HAMILTON, L. D. (1960). *J. Mol. Biol.*, **2**, 19.

LANGRIDGE, R., MARVIN, D. A., SEEDS, W. E., WILSON, H. R., HOOPER, C. W., WILKINS, M. H. F. and HAMILTON, L. D. (1960). *J. Mol. Biol.*, **2**, 38.

LEONARD, B. R., ANDEREGG, J. W., SCHULMAN, S., KAESBERG, P. and BEEMAN, W. W. (1953). *Biochim. Biophys. Acta*, **12**, 499.

LIPSON, H. and COCHRAN, W. (1953). *The Determination of Crystal Structures.* London: Bell.

LUZZATI, V., NICOLAIEFF, A. and MASSON, F. (1961). *J. Mol. Biol.*, **3**, 185.

LUZZATI, V., LUZZATI, D. and MASSON, F. (1962). *J. Mol. Biol.*, **5**, 375.

LUZZATI, V. and NICOLAIEFF, A. (1963). *J. Mol. Biol.*, **7**, 142.

MACARTHUR, I. (1943). *Nature*, **152**, 38.

MAGDOFF, B. E. (1960). *Nature*, **185**, 673.

MARKHAM, R., HITCHBORN, J. H., HILLS, G. J. and FREY, S. (1964). *Virology*, **22**, 342.

MARSH, R. E., COREY, R. B. and PAULING, L. (1955a). *Biochim. Biophys. Acta*, **16**, 1.

MARSH, R. E., COREY, R. B. and PAULING, L. (1955b). *Acta Cryst.*, **8**, 710.

MARVIN, D. A., SPENCER, M., WILKINS, M. H. F. and HAMILTON, L. D. (1961). *J. Mol. Biol.*, **2**, 19.

MATHEWS, F. S. and RICH, A. (1964). *J. Mol. Biol.*, **8**, 89.

MEYER, K. H. and MARK. H. (1928) *Ber. dtsch Chem. Ges.*, **361**, 192.

MUIRHEAD, H. and PERUTZ, M. F. (1963). *Nature*, **199**, 633.

NIXON, H. J. and GIBBS, A. J. (1960). *J. Mol. Biol.*, **2**, 197.

O'BRIEN, E. J. (1963). *J. Mol. Biol.*, **7**, 107.

PARKER, K. D. and RUDALL, K. M. (1957). *Nature*, **179**, 905.

PATTERSON, A. L. (1934). *Phys. Rev.*, **46**, 372.

PAULING, L., COREY, R. B. and BRANSON, H. R. (1951). *Proc. Nat. Acad. Sci. U.S.A.*, **37**, 205.

PAULING, L. and COREY, R. B. (1951a). *Proc. Nat. Acad. Sci. U.S.A.*, **37**, 235.

PAULING, L. and COREY, R. B. (1951b). *Proc. Nat. Acad. Sci. U.S.A.*, **37**, 241.

PAULING, L. and COREY, R. B. (1951c). *Proc. Nat. Acad. Sci. U.S.A.*, **37**, 251.

PAULING, L. and COREY, R. B. (1951d). *Proc. Nat. Acad. Sci. U.S.A.*, **37**, 256.

PAULING, L. and COREY, R. B. (1951e). *Proc. Nat. Acad. Sci. U.S.A.*, **37**, 261.

PAULING, L. and COREY, R. B. (1951f). *Proc. Nat. Acad. Sci. U.S.A.*, **37**, 271.

PAULING, L. and COREY, R. B. (1951g). *Proc. Nat. Acad. Sci. U.S.A.*, **37**, 282.

PAULING, L. and COREY, R. B. (1951h). *Proc. Nat. Acad. Sci. U.S.A.*, **37**, 729.

PAULING, L. and COREY, R. B. (1953a). *Proc. Nat. Acad. Sci. U.S.A.*, **39**, 253.

PAULING, L. and COREY, R. B. (1953b). *Nature*, **171**, 59.

PEERDEMAN, A. F., BOMMEL, A. J. and BIJVOET, (1951). *Nature*, **168**, 271.

PERUTZ, M. F. (1951). *Nature*, **167**, 1053.

PERUTZ, M. F., ROSSMANN, M. G., CULLIS, A. F., MUIRHEAD, H., WILL, G. and NORTH, A. C. T. (1960). *Nature*, **185**, 416.

PERUTZ, M. F., BOLTON, W., DIAMOND, R., MUIRHEAD, H. and WATSON, H. C. (1964). *Nature*, **203**, 687.

PRESTON, G. D. (1944). *J. Sci. Inst.*, **21**, 205.

RAMACHANDRAN, G. N. (1960). *Proc. Indian Acad. Sci.*, **52**, 240.

RAMACHANDRAN, G. N. and KARTHA, G. (1954). *Nature*, **174**, 269.

RAMACHANDRAN, G. N. and KARTHA, G. (1955). *Nature*, **176**, 593.

RAMACHANDRAN, G. N. and RAMAN, S. (1956). *Current Science* (India), **25**, 348.

RAMACHANDRAN, G. N., SASISEKHARAN, V. and THATHACHARI, Y. T. (1962). In *Collagen*. Ed. N. RAMANATHAN. New York: Interscience.

RICH, A. (1957). *Ann. N.Y. Acad. Sci.*, Special Publ. **5**, 186.

RICH, A. (1958). *Nature*, **181**, 521.

RICH, A. and WATSON, J. D. (1954a). *Nature*, **173**, 995.

RICH, A. and WATSON, J. D. (1954b). *Proc. Nat. Acad. Sci. U.S.A.*, **40**, 759.

RICH, A. and CRICK, F. H. C. (1955). *Nature*, **176**, 915.

RICH, A. and CRICK, F. H. C. (1961). *J. Mol. Biol.*, **3**, 483.

RICH, A. and DAVIES, D. R. (1956). *J. Amer. Chem. Soc.*, **78**, 3548.

RICH, A., DAVIES, D. R., CRICK, F. H. C. and WATSON, J. D. (1961). *J. Mol. Biol.*, **3**, 71.

RILEY, D. P. and OSTER, G. (1951). *Biochim. Biophys. Acta*, **7**, 526.

ROBERTSON, J. M. (1936). *J. Chem. Soc.*, **225**, 1195.

ROGULENKOVA, V. N., MILLIONOVA, M. I. and ANDREEVA, N. S. (1964). *J. Mol. Biol.*, **9**, 253.

ROSSMANN, M. G. (1960). *Acta Cryst.*, **13,** 221.

ROSSMANN, M. G. and BLOW, D. M. (1961). *Acta Cryst.*, **14,** 641.

ROSSMANN, M. G. and BLOW, D. M. (1963). *Acta Cryst.*, **16,** 39.

RUDALL, K. M. (1962). *Comparative Biochemistry.* Eds. M. FLORKIN and H. S. MASON, Vol. 4, p. 397. New York: Academic Press.

SASISEKHARAN, V. (1959). *Acta Cryst.*, **12,** 903.

SCHMIDT, P., KAESBERG, P. and BEEMAN, W. W. (1954). *Biochim. Biophys. Acta*, **14,** 1.

SOBELL, H. M., TOMITA, K. and RICH, A. (1963). *Proc. Nat. Acad. Sci. U.S.A.*, **49,** 885.

SPENCER, M., FULLER, W., WILKINS, M. H. F. and BROWN, G. L. (1962). *Nature*, **194,** 1014.

SPENCER, M. and POOLE, F. (1965) *J. Mol. Biol.*, **11,** 314.

STOKES, A. R. (1955a). *Acta Cryst.*, **8,** 27.

STOKES, A. R. (1955b). *Progr. in Biophys.*, **5,** 140.

TAYLOR, C. A. and LIPSON, H. (1964). *Optical Transforms.* London: Bell.

TOMITA, K. and RICH, A. (1964). *Nature*, **201,** 1160.

TROMMEL, J. and BIJVOET, J. M. (1954). *Acta Cryst.*, **7,** 703.

WATSON, J. D. (1954). *Biochim. Biophys. Acta*, **13,** 10.

WATSON, J. D. and CRICK, F. H. C. (1953a). *Nature*, **171,** 737.

WATSON, J. D. and CRICK, F. H. C. (1953b). *Nature*, **171,** 964.

WILKINS, M. H. F. (1956). *Cold Spring Harbor Symp. Quant. Biol.*, **21,** 75.

WILKINS, M. H. F. and BATTAGLIA, (1953). *Biochim. Biophys. Acta*, **11,** 412.

WILKINS, M. H. F., SEEDS, W. E., STOKES, A. R. and WILSON, H. R. (1953). *Nature*, **172,** 759.

WILKINS, M. H. F., STOKES, A. R. and WILSON, H. R. (1953). *Nature*, **171,** 737.

WILKINS, M. H. F. and RANDALL, J. T. (1953). *Biochim. Biophys. Acta* **10,** 192.

WILKINS, M. H. F., ZUBAY, G. and WILSON, H. R. (1959). *J. Mol. Biol.*, **1,** 179

WILLIAMS, R. C. and SMITH, K. M. (1958). *Biochim. Biophys. Acta*, **28,** 464

WILSON, A. J. C. (1942). *Nature*, **150,** 152.

ZUBAY, G. and WILKINS, M. H. F. (1960). *J. Mol. Biol.*, **2,** 105.

Index